The Instrument Pilot's Library
• Volume Seven •

The Point of Decision

by
The Editors of *IFR* and *IFR Refresher*

Belvoir Publications, Inc.
Greenwich, Connecticut

ISBN: 1-879620-30-8

Printed and bound in the United States of America by Quebecor Printing, Fairfield, Pennsylvania.

Contents

Preface

The vast majority of the time we spend flying is taken up with the commonplace and routine. Cruising along in a straight line requires little of the pilot. The remainder of the flight, though, is full of crucial moments and decisions; the pilot must make the right choices and act appropriately, or disaster could result.

These decisions and critical moments are what this book is all about.

Previous volumes in the *Instrument Pilot's Library* have covered individual aspects of instrument flight in detail. For this seventh book, we'll take a step back and look at the big picture. The topics covered here run the gamut from weather to self-evaluation to flying technique. While the territory covered is broad, all of the articles found here share a common thread; the critical moment at which a decision must be made.

When we say "decision," the image that immediately springs to mind is that of the big, operational question: Do I go or not? Do I turn back? Do I have enough fuel to make it?

But, flying is full of more immediate, skill-related decisions as well. How do you know it's time to abort a takeoff? When do you choose to go around? We'll discuss those decisions as well.

Also, there are the decisions related to your fitness to fly. Are you really competent, today, right now, to make a flight? How do you decide that you're not?

We'll discuss all of these topics and more in this book. As with all the books in this series, our objective is not to offer a textbook. Rather, we aim to help you make better use of the knowledge you already have.

• Section One •

Case
Histories

Decide: Press On or Turn Back?

W e'll start off with a case history, the story of a classic decision-based accident that happened a dozen years ago. This accident deals with one kind of decision an instrument pilot must make: The decision to press on or abort in the face of deteriorating conditions.

This is one of the toughest choices there is, because a pilot on the spot may not perceive the situation as being as bad as it actually is. It's a gray area that each pilot defines for him- or herself. How bad is too bad? What makes you turn back? Read on, assess your own decisions objectively, and see if you would have turned back before it was too late.

Press On Home

It's that old "home field advantage." Some pilots seem to feel that once a flight has begun, there is no going back, that they cannot return to their departure point and wait for the weather to improve. These pilots sometimes find themselves trapped, and the escape routes can vanish in the flick of an eye.

"Having started, the flight had to terminate somewhere," the pilot wrote after the accident. But perhaps not where intended. The story of his flight contains many lessons.

The 59-year-old, 999-hour pilot of a Cessna 172 found himself trapped by icing and below minimums as he attempted to shoot a "modified" ILS into Greater Rockford Airport, Rockford, Illinois. The Cessna was destroyed when it hit trees and a building near the approach end of the runway in the January 23, 1983 accident. Fortunately, by incredible luck, the pilot did not terminate where the flight did—he escaped with minor injuries.

The pilot was rated and current for the flight. He held a private certificate with instrument rating, and had logged some 105 hours of instrument flight, 68 of which were in actual instrument conditions.

He was about to embark on a flight that would illustrate the incredible lure of the home airport, and the many small indecisions and mistakes that can tally up to one all-or-nothing roll of the dice. Perhaps the biggest single lesson is that there is nothing inevitable about a trip that starts VFR and ends in an approach to below-minimums weather.

Beginnings

The pilot had spent the preceding two days skiing with a church youth group near Ironwood, Michigan. The youth group was planning to stay at Ironwood through the weekend, but the pilot wanted to get home to Rockford by Saturday evening to attend a church meeting on Sunday morning.

The adventure started at about 3:45 on Saturday afternoon when the pilot radioed the FSS at Houghton, Michigan from Ironwood, Michigan. He filed an IFR flight plan for a trip from Ironwood to Rockford, with a departure time "as soon as possible," according to the statement of the FSS specialist. He listed Madison, Wisconsin as his alternate.

There is a dispute on the record concerning a weather briefing. The investigator, in the accident factual report, asserts that "the pilot stated that he received a preflight weather briefing from Houghton FSS...via radio telephone. However, the FSS specialist at Houghton stated: A pilot weather brief was not given."

But according to the pilot, he had received a briefing. Contacted by telephone, he told us, "The FSS hadn't recorded it immediately, but there was definitely a briefing given." He could not recall what the weather was for his route during our interview. (We were, however, able to obtain the weather observations which he might have been given in his briefing.)

The weather at his departure point, according to the pilot's observation, was "gorgeous...a beautiful day." (Indeed, the observation taken at Houghton, Michigan at 2:52 p.m. local time listed conditions as a clear sky with a visibility of 40 miles.)

But weather at points along his route was not so nice. The 2:52 observation at Madison, Wisconsin (the alternate): sky obscured, measured ceiling 500 overcast, visibility three-quarters of a mile, light snow and fog. (The lowest published approach for Madison, the VOR-B approach, had minimums of 700 feet and one mile.)

And Rockford, his destination, at 3:12 p.m. recorded a special observation: measured ceiling 500 overcast, seven miles visibility.

Cedar Rapids, Iowa, offered a hint of what was to come for the Rockford area, though. The 2:52 observation: 600-foot obscured ceiling, visibility varying around two miles in light snow and fog.

But even the most complete weather briefing could not have prepared him for what lay in wait. There was no icing forecast for the area. But moderate mixed icing did exist, however, and would figure in the final outcome.

Decision Point 1:
Options: Get more weather information; wait for weather system to pass; *embark on flight*. [Pilot's choice in italics-Ed.]

Starting Small

By 3:56, the Skyhawk was in the air and the flight plan was activated. The pilot later reported that he had departed in VFR conditions from Ironwood. Weather at the destination had deteriorated somewhat. Rockford reported at 3:51 that the ceiling had fallen to a measured 400-foot overcast with five miles visibility in fog. His alternate at Madison: sky obscured, 400 feet scattered, measured 500 feet overcast, visiblity one-half mile.

The flight progressed uneventfully for the first hour and a half darkness began to close in. The C-172 now began to pick up some rime ice, according to the pilot's statement in his accident report. The pilot later wrote, "I turned on my landing light and realized I was flying through light snowfall. I looked at the corners of my windshield to see if any ice was forming. There was a slight accumulation. Taking my flashlight, I turned the beam on the leading edge of the wing. A light coat of ice was forming."

Decision Point 2:
Options: Return to Ironwood; get more weather info; *continue the flight and try to get clear of ice*.

He requested a climb (from 7,000 feet to 8,000) to try to get away from the ice. He did not mention the ice to ATC at this time. The controller told the pilot that 8,000 feet and a little north of Madison would put the flight between layers. The pilot found this was true, and "the ice which had formed quickly sublimated." After passing Madison, ATC called for the Cessna to descend down to 7,000 feet and turned the flight over to Rockford Approach.

The approach controller gave the pilot the current Rockford weather. This was the first time since takeoff that the pilot had received any updated weather information, according to the accident report. The news was not good. Rockford had dropped to an indefinite ceiling of 100 feet obscured, visibility half a mile in fog and light drizzle. The destination was below minimums.

Decision Point 3:
Options: Get more weather info and divert to a field with weather above minimums; *press on, hoping conditions will somehow improve without requiring a decision.*

About 12 minutes later, the controller informed the pilot that the RVR at Rockford had dropped to 2,400. "Its been on the downward trend here for the last 20 minutes or so." the controller said. The controller thought of a field about 30 miles north of Rockford. "Do you want me to check to see what Janesville's got for weather?"

Decisions, Decisions
About a minute later, the controller came back with the Janesville weather: "Estimated 500 overcast. visibility one and a half with fog. Wind 060 at five. Janesville altimeter two nine eight six. Their glideslope is out of service, but if that ceiling is good estimated at 500 feet, that still gives you minimums for the approach." (The minimums for a localizer 4 approach at Janesville were indeed 500 and one-half.)

"Glideslope out, you say?" the pilot asked. The controller confirmed that the glideslope was not working.

"Okay," the pilot asked, "what runway would we use?"

"Probably runway 4, straight in off the ILS with the wind 060 at five." the controller shot back.

Decision Point 4:
Options: Seek more weather info and divert elsewhere; continue to Rockford; *try the controller's suggestion—Janesville.*

The pilot didn't ponder long. "Okay, let's go in up there."

Meanwhile, weather in the rest of the area was changing. Madison was now reporting a 400-foot overcast, but visibilities had improved to five miles in light snow and fog. Cedar Rapids, Iowa—just west of Rockford—reported an obscured 800-foot ceiling, visibility varying from two miles to one and a quarter miles in drizzle and fog. Weather at Chicago, to the east, was 600 feet overcast, visibility seven miles in light snow. None of this information was relayed to the pilot, nor did he request it.

First Attempt

The controller issued a vector to the northwest, outbound from the Janesville VOR, and called for a descent down to 2,700 feet. "Report leaving 4,000." the controller told him. "I'll start your turn back inbound at that time."

"Descending to 2,700 feet resulted in an immediate build-up of ice on the leading edge of the wing as the plane descended from a much colder altitude." the pilot later wrote. Transcripts show that he never mentioned this to the controller, however.

Decision Point 5:
Options: Treat the icing conditions as an emergency; *say nothing and continue.*

The Cessna was vectored to the localizer and cleared for the approach six miles from the outer marker. But as the Cessna got closer, the pilot asked the controller to, "monitor this thing as I come over [the outer marker]. I'm not sure this localizer is working."

"All right." the controller responded, "I show you just about on it right now." The pilot reported that his needle hadn't moved. The controller told him that radar showed the Cessna right on the localizer. "Okay," the pilot said, "This localizer. I don't think this localizer is working. We may have to come to Rockford and use the NDB."

The controller's response: "Okay, well, fly a heading of 040 for now. Let me know if you get the localizer. If not, why, we'll vector you to Rockford. What frequency you got set for the localizer there?"

"[I'm] not picking up the localizer." the pilot called.

"You say you are now?" the controller asked.

"We're not." the pilot reiterated.

"What frequency do you have set on the localizer?" the controller tried to confirm his radio setting.

"One oh nine point one." the pilot responded.

"Okay, that's the right frequency." the controller told him.

Decision Point 6:
Options: Get more info and divert elsewhere; *try Rockford no matter how low it is.*

"We'll try Rockford no matter how low it is." the pilot said, breaking off the approach.

The controller gave him a climb to 3,000 feet and a heading back towards Rockford, telling the pilot that the RVR at Rockford was now up to 2,000. "Beautiful." was the pilot's reply.

Things Change

Two minutes later, the controller told the pilot that the RVR had now dropped to 1,800 feet. He asked the pilot how much fuel he had on board. "Probably got two hours, a little less than two hours." the pilot said.

The controller brought the Cessna around for an ILS approach to Rockford's runway 36. Weather at the time was reported as indefinite ceiling 100 feet obscured, visibility half a mile in fog. Winds were given as 080 at five.

Realizing his localizer receiver was out, the pilot asked the controller to "give us like a no gyro approach. You can monitor it as I come on down."

"Well, we can do that." the controller replied. "I just checked with Janesville. They said their localizer, they checked it out, the maintenance man says it's working."

"I don't think it's their localizer." the pilot said, "I think it's this thing."

The pilot later told us "by this time, ice was forming more heavily and the propeller was vibrating. An occasional thump was heard as ice apparently broke loose and hit the fuselage. I realized it was becoming most urgent that I get the plane on the ground, or assuredly it would do it on its own." He did not tell the controller about this, though.

Decision Point 7:
Options: Declare an emergency due to ice, maintain altitude and exit from icing conditions; *press on silently.*

Old College Try

The controller started hunting around for alternates for the pilot. The closest better weather was at Madison. Five minutes after their regular observation at 6:50, observers there issued a special observation: 400-foot overcast with one mile visibility in light snow and fog. But this was still too low for the approaches available, and the Madison weather would continue to get worse.

The controller relayed this information to the pilot, who replied, "Okay, let's see what we can do here."

"Okay," the controller told him, "the RVR is still 1,800 here at Rockford...and our visibility now, ah, prevailing visibility is a quarter mile in light drizzle and fog."

Decision Point 8:
Options: Get more weather info ("What's Chicago got? How about Cedar Rapids? Could I make it to Oshkosh?") and divert; *continue to Rockford for the "old college try. "*

"Okay, we'll give it the old college try." the pilot said.
    Why didn't he divert? Why didn't he look for better weather? "Rockford's my home base," he later told us. "I'd made that approach hundreds of times. I was familiar with the terrain and the approach, so I thought I'd try there."
    Meanwhile, weather over the rest of the region had deteriorated. Madison was below minimums. Chicago, which was reporting a variable 600-foot overcast with visibility seven miles in light snow, "was not even mentioned," the pilot said. This was the best weather in the local area, however.
    Cedar Rapids, to the west, was slightly better with an 800-foot obscured ceiling and two miles visibility in light snow and fog. The controller didn't mention this, either, but of course, he hadn't been asked.
    At this point, even turning around and going back to the north was becoming a questionable option. Houghton, Michigan had fallen to a 500-foot broken overcast. Oshkosh, Wisconsin now offered the best weather within reach, with an estimated 1,500-foot overcast and three miles visibility during the 6:47 p.m. observation. This was deteriorating, though, and by the time of the next observation, one hour later, the ceiling had fallen to a 700-foot obscured ceiling with one mile visibility.

A New Approach
"What are your intentions?" the controller queried. "What kind of approach do you want to make, sir?"

Decision Point 9:
Options: Get more weather info and divert; *create a home-brewed approach procedure and try it.*

"I'd like the ILS and, I think the glideslope's still working on this thing, but the localizer is out and we'll use the NDB to help us down." the pilot opted.
    "You want to fly an ILS without a localizer and you're going to fly the glideslope and the NDB, is that correct?" the controller asked.
    "Yes, yes that's affirmative," the pilot replied.
    The controller chose a more helpful option.

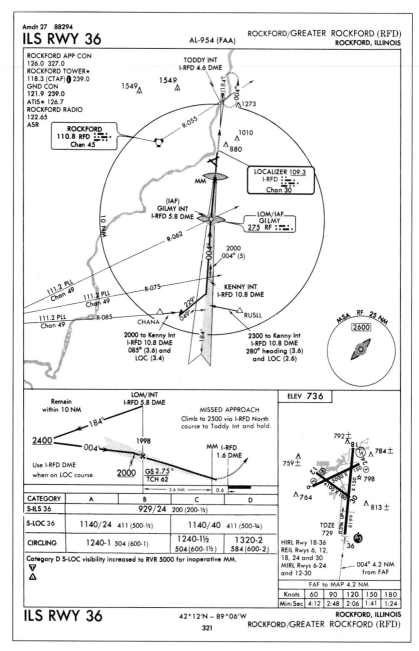

With no localizer, the pilot wanted to try a home-brewed approach using the LOM for course guidance and the glideslope. He settled for the controller's suggestion of an ASR approach.

He offered to provide headings down the approach using Airport Surveillance Radar. The pilot replied, "That'll be super."

Now came the final series of events, and it would have all the appearance of inevitability.

The controller told Skyhawk N61558 to turn to a heading of 200, and had the pilot confirm his altitude as 3,000 feet. "Affirmative," the pilot replied. "Where we at now for five five eight?"

"You are four miles northwest of the airport," the controller told him. "Okay," the pilot replied.

"Five five eight, the runway 36 RVR is now 1,600," the controller passed along.

"It's a little better." the pilot said.

"No, it's a little worse. It was 1,800 before." the controller told him.

"Okay, (unintelligible) tonight. Where's five five eight now?" the pilot asked.

"Your position is about three miles west-southwest of the airport." the controller offered.

"Okay, we'd like to turn in as quickly as possible," the pilot stated.

The controller called for descent to 2,500 feet and, after confirming what frequency the Cessna was using, turned him over to the ASR controller.

Last Attempt

The pilot switched frequencies and the approach started. "Okay, five five eight's with you," the pilot called.

"Cessna five five eight, radio check. How do you hear?" the ASR controller queried. "Real great, loud and clear," came the reply.

The ASR controller started right up. "Five five eight, roger, fly heading 180, maintain 2,300. Be vectors, surveillance final approach course runway 36. The minimum descent altitude 1,160 feet, the missed approach point is the runway threshold. In the event of lost communications, climb and maintain 2,500 feet, proceed direct to Gilmy outer compass locator and execute the full ILS or NDB, whichever you have the equipment for."

"Roger, five five eight," the pilot replied.

"And five five eight, verify you're on a 180 heading."

"Let me check this thing," the pilot said.

"Hold it. I think we got to move this compass over. We reset our compass."

"Five five eight, roger." the ASR controller said. "Fly heading 180. I will be turning you on the final five miles from the runway to give you time to line up on the runway."

"Okay, good deal." came the response.

"I knew it was going to be a tight approach," the pilot later wrote, "and would take all the concentration I could muster. In preparation for the final approach. I cinched my lap and shoulder harness as tight as possible."

"Runway 36 visual range now 1,600," the controller told him, "and if no transmissions received for one minute on the vector or fifteen seconds on the final, execute the published missed approach procedure."

"Roger." the pilot said.

"Cessna five five eight, would you like recommended altitudes on the final?" the controller asked.

"Wouldn't mind."

"Okay." the controller said

"Take all the help I can get tonight," the pilot told him.

"Cessna five five eight, the wind direction is estimated, the indicators at the tower are out of service at this time. Weather bureau last sequence gave us winds at 100 at six knots," the controller told him.

"Roger," the pilot replied. The Cessna was now on a left downwind about four miles south-southwest of the airport.

"Cessna five five eight, say your altitude."

"We're at 2,200 right now," the pilot told him.

"Altitude should be 2,300," the controller reminded him. But the pilot replied, "I don't know if we can pull her up. We're picking up a little bit of ice." This was the first time the pilot mentioned the icing.

"Cessna five five eight, roger," the controller said, "Turn left heading 090 and attempt to maintain 2,300 and the altimeter is two niner eight six."

"Roger. What was that heading?"

"090. We're turning a left base leg now for the approach," the controller replied.

"Roger. 090." was all the pilot said

Wandering

The Cessna was now five miles south of the airport on the left base leg of the approach. The pilot radioed that he was maintaining the 2,300 foot altitude requested.

"Roger," the controller said. "verify you're on an east heading 090."

"We're a little bit to the left. We'll be right back there." the pilot said.

The controller told him the RVR was 1,600 again. "Okay, five five eight. we know." the pilot replied.

"Cessna five five eight, prepare to begin descent in one mile. Published minimum descent altitude 1,160 feet. Turn left heading 060."

"Left to 060 and we're at 2,300 feet." the pilot stated.

"Cessna five five eight you can begin descent to your minimum descent altitude and let me know if you're receiving the glideslope. You're four and one-half miles south of the airport." The controller was now into the final approach phase.

"Just passing Gilmy [the outer marker] inbound," the pilot called as he pulled on the carburetor heat. This, as the pilot later realized, was probably a mistake that robbed him of some vital engine rpms.

"Five five eight, that's correct and heading should be 060. You're left of course and correcting nicely and you're descending to your minimum descent altitude, is that correct?"

"Ah, that's affirmative," the pilot replied.

The Cessna was again drifting to the left of course as it came down the approach. The controller steered him back to the centerline and gave him a heading of 020, but he started drifting off to the left again. The controller gave him a turn to 030. The Cessna remained "slightly left of course and correcting nicely."

Last Words

"Turn left heading 020," the controller told him. "You're drifting right of course rapidly. You're very slightly right of course and correcting back to course."

"You're one-half mile from runway. You're very slightly left of course now. Turn right heading 030." The post-accident weather observation would reveal the RVR had now dropped to 800 feet.

The Cessna disappeared from the scope. The controller called, "Cessna five five eight, Rockford, how do you hear?" But there was no reply.

The pilot later reported that he was coming down the approach and having difficulty maintaining airspeed. "I think what happened," he later told a local reporter, "was the plane was loaded with ice. I was keeping the power up. The tower was talking me down. I didn't have the radios I normally have. I thought I was higher than I was and I pulled the throttle back a bit. The plane sank like crazy."

Perhaps slightly rattled by the controller's call of "You're drifting right of course rapidly." the pilot gave a harder twist on the yoke than he should have. The 172 veered to the west, making almost a right angle to the approach course. According to the accident factual report, the final resting place of the Cessna was a straight line about 90 degrees left of the approach course from where it disappeared from the radar screen.

The pilot was about to make visual contact. "I saw a flash that lit up the windshield." he told us. " Then I looked up and saw another flash, and the next thing I saw was the trees." In his accident report, the pilot stated that after hitting the tree "the plane cartwheeled to the left, and after hitting another tree, collided with an unoccupied building." The Cessna's wing rode up the roof of the building, rolling the plane inverted before it hit the wall. It stopped, and dropped to the ground upside-down in front of the building.

The controller knew the Cessna had crashed. He called out the equipment and requested a special weather observation. Within ten minutes the Cessna had been found. It had slammed into the side of Camp Elmwood Singing Society Lodge a quarter mile west of the approach lights for runway 36. The pilot kicked out one of the side windows and crawled out of the wreckage. Rescuers arrived to find him "walking around," according to a local newspaper account. He had survived with only bruises and a cut on his ear from his skis, which "came flying through the cabin at the moment of impact." One of the pilot's friends was quoted as saying. "He was smiling and didn't seem to be in shock or anything."

"Sometimes the good Lord is sitting on your shoulder," the pilot told reporters. "It just wasn't my time."

The Investigation

The post-accident investigation confirmed that the localizer converter aboard the Cessna was not working. The probable cause of the accident, however, was laid to the pilot's "inadequate" preflight planning and preparation, his supposed failure to get a weather briefing and his flight into known adverse weather.

His own analysis of the accident? "A case could be made that the flight should not have been initiated. But having started, it had to be terminated somewhere. In the opinion of the pilot, the accident would have been less likely to occur if the primary ILS receiver had been operating, icing had not accumulated during descent and not complicated by marginal panel lighting.

"[The] pilot also recognizes that he utilized carburetor heat on the approach and just prior to crash had reduced rpm by 100 to 200. This was [a] lesson not to be forgotten; that under icing conditions, the pilot should maintain the highest power level right down to runway threshhold." He told us in a telephone interview that, "My mistake was that I thought I was real high at the middle marker and I pulled power at a high angle of attack. She quit flying and dropped real fast. An FAA man later told me that if I hadn't pulled the power, I'd have flown right onto the runway."

The Feds Step In

Indeed. the FAA had taken notice of the accident. "About a week later." the pilot wrote, "I received a letter from the FAA indicating that my recent accident had raised a question about my competency to fly IFR and requested that I make an appointment for a review of the flight and a re-examination of my flight maneuvers.

"On the appointed day, in a rented plane, I flew to the regional FAA office located at DuPage County Airport. I was introduced to the FAA flight examiner and we proceeded to a conference room. Here we reviewed all my logbooks. Then we reviewed the conditions of my flight. The flight examiner took considerable time and patience to explain the circumstances so that if I ever encountered this situation again I would be well prepared.

"There was a question concerning my flight briefing [prior to take-off]. The NTSB had initially reported that the briefer stated that I was not given a briefing because 'he was in a hurry to get going.' Fortunately, I had kept a copy of my briefing which was recovered from the plane and I was able to give a detailed report of the conversation with the briefer. Later, a more thorough check of the Houghton FSS records did list the briefing. However, the examiner suggested that should I ever get a briefing in a remote area by telephone or radio to request the initials of the briefer. This will serve to confirm that a briefing was conducted should a question ever be raised." [This is a new one to us. Who's *really* going to go around taking names?—Ed.]

The FAA man had other lessons for the pilot. "Keep the throttle wide open right down to the runway threshold and then pull the power. Better a fast landing and the application of brakes to landing short. Brakes are less expensive to replace than an entire airplane.

"Finally, I have a greater respect for the spread between temperature and dewpoint. Never again will I take off when the spread between temperature and dewpoint is less than five degrees at the arrival airport. The 600-foot reported ceiling and the actual conditions at the airport three hours later gave airport proof of how fast conditions change when nightfall occurs."

Proper Restraint

One thing he felt fortunate for was his restraint system. "The plane hit the trees and did a flip," he later said. "It's a good thing I had my belts on. I was wearing both my seatbelt and shoulder harness. I'm sore all over. Everyplace where my safety belts cut into my hips and chest hurts. It feels like I've been in a football game." Cinching the belts down tight during the approach probably saved him from more severe injuries.

He's still flying, too. "As it [the 172] hit the ground, I sold it to the insurance company." he said. He bought another Skyhawk.

"My wife was never too hot on my flying," he told a local newspaper after the accident. "I feel I made some mistakes, but it's no worse than a car accident. I've had some of those and you don't stop driving. I'll go right back up and fly."

And he did. He told us, "After completing my review with the FAA, I purchased a new airplane and continue to fly a little older and less bolder and thankful to the good Lord who watches over pilots who wander into some difficult situations."

The Point

We'd argue that the pilot's assessment of where he went wrong (well into the flight, after the weather had deteriorated, and he discovered that his localizer receiver was not working) was late.

Had he been more conservative, he may well have diverted much earlier. As we've shown here, there were no fewer than five distinct times at which he was presented with a point of decision prior to his report of a failed radio. Making the choice to turn and run sooner could have prevented the accident. Also, the controller may have been able to suggest alternate destinations or altitudes had he been aware of the pilot's icing situation earlier.

This, of course, amounts to Monday-morning quarterbacking. We weren't there, and it's possible things didn't look nearly bad enough at the time to warrant an abort.

Making the "right" choice is what this book is all about, though. Knowing the situation, what would *you* have done?

Pulling the Plug
in Time

The last accident was typical of IFR mishaps in that it reflected the common mistake of pressing on in the face of deteriorating conditions. Much less common is the sort of accident we have here: An instructional flight made in VFR conditions ended in tragedy at least in part because the instructor did not decide to pull the plug in time. The student also failed to realize (or failed to admit) that he was getting in over his head.

This is something that many of us have experienced in training. In an attempt to do well in training, or to pass a checkride, we get into a situation that exceeds our abilities. Usually it becomes obvious before there's any real danger, the instructor will take control, and everyone involved will learn from the experience.

But it's important to recognize the moment when you're no longer in control of the situation. If you're an instructor, you must learn to recognize that point in the student, and act appropriately, before it's too late.

A Simulation Gets Real

Flight training carries with it some inherent dangers: An instructor must be careful, when simulating an emergency, not to complicate the situation to the point where a real emergency develops. In this accident the instructor introduced several equipment failures that induced spatial disorientation while flying an instrument approach in VMC at night. A crash resulted and the careers of three young commuter airline pilots were cut short.

The pilots were flying a Beechcraft 1900C, a 19-passenger twin-engine turboprop operated by their company. The purpose of the flight was to train the pilot in the left seat so he could upgrade to captain. He was an ATP with more than 2500 hours total time and 1200 hours in the Beech 1900. In the right seat was a captain who was an ATP, instructor and company check pilot. He had more than 5600 hours total time, with more than 1100 hours in the Beech 1900. The third pilot was another captain-trainee riding along to observe the training session.

VFR Operation

The flight departed Bridgeport, Connecticut at 6:45 on a December night. The weather was clear and 20 miles visibility, with westerly winds at 12 knots. The pilots operated VFR and never talked to ATC, except for the tower at Bridgeport when departing. They proceeded eastbound across Long Island Sound and conducted a series of instrument approaches at Block Island State Airport, which is 14 nm east of Long Island and 34 nm south-southwest of Providence, Rhode Island.

At 8 p.m., the crew landed at Block Island and took a break. Witnesses reported the three pilots discussed the technical aspects of the airplane and seemed in good spirits; everything to suggest a normal training session. The crew departed about an hour later.

The National Transportation Safety Board pieced together the remainder of the flight using the airplane's cockpit voice recorder and ATC recorded radar data. The crew took off and briefed for the NDB Runway 10 at Block Island with a circle-to-land Runway 28. After completing the approach briefing, the instructor failed the captain-trainee's electrically-powered attitude indicator by pulling the circuit breaker.

The trainee identified the failure and turned direct to the NDB (their conversation indicated they were eight miles out). They had departed Runway 28 and were most likely west of the field. Assuming a position west of the NDB, they should have flown to the NDB, then turned almost 180 degrees in order to track 286 outbound (see the NDB approach chart). The conversation that followed indicated the trainee was confused about his position on the approach:

"I'll be going to the beacon, then it'll he right-hand turns, parallel entry."

"What's this parallel entry stuff?" queried the instructor.

"Oh, I'm sorry, it's after the missed," replied the trainee.

If they were inbound from the west, he might have believed they were already on the approach.

Then the conversation reflects the trainee-captain was distracted by the failed attitude indicator:

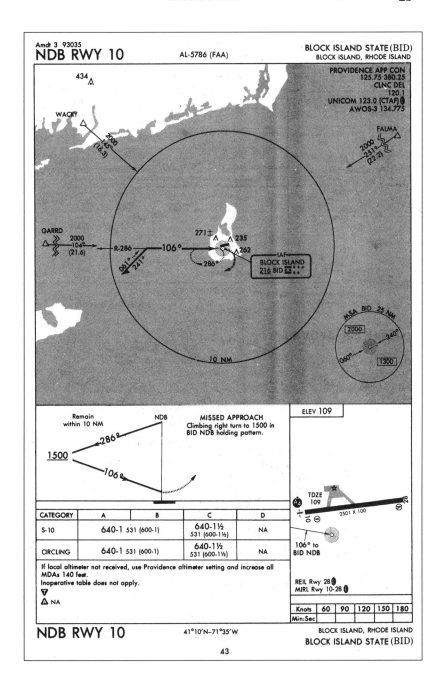

Amdt 3 93035

NDB RWY 10

AL-5786 (FAA)

BLOCK ISLAND STATE (BID)
BLOCK ISLAND, RHODE ISLAND

PROVIDENCE APP CON
125.75 380.25
CLNC DEL
120.1
UNICOM 123.0 (CTAF)
AWOS-3 134.775

434

WACKY

2000
145°
(13.5)

FALMA

2000
251°
(22.2)

GARRD

2000
104°
(21.6)

R-286

106°

271±

235

262

286°

241°

061°

IAF
BLOCK ISLAND
216 BID

MSA BID 25 NM

2000

240°

060°

1300

10 NM

Remain
within 10 NM

NDB

286°

1500

106°

MISSED APPROACH
Climbing right turn to 1500 in
BID NDB holding pattern.

ELEV 109

TDZE
109

2501 X 100

106° to
BID NDB

REIL Rwy 28
MIRL Rwy 10-28

CATEGORY	A	B	C	D
S-10	640-1 531 (600-1)		640-1½ 531 (600-1½)	NA
CIRCLING	640-1 531 (600-1)		640-1½ 531 (600-1½)	NA

If local altimeter not received, use Providence altimeter setting and increase all
MDAs 140 feet.
Inoperative table does not apply.
▽
△ NA

Knots	60	90	120	150	180
Min:Sec					

NDB RWY 10

41°10'N–71°35'W

BLOCK ISLAND, RHODE ISLAND
BLOCK ISLAND STATE (BID)

43

"It'd be easier if you'd just cover that thing up...I guess I gotta force myself to ignore it."

He had a good point. When the AI fails, it's a good idea to cover the instrument so you'll omit it from your scan and avoid getting distracted.

In what was probably an effort to ensure things went smoothly, the instructor quizzed the trainee about how they would fly each segment of the approach. The trainee's responses still indicated uncertainty about what should have been a straightforward approach.

As they crossed the NDB outbound for the approach, the trainee had continued difficulty controlling the airplane under partial panel, which prompted the following comments from the instructor:

"Watch what you're doing...your DG is your primary bank and your altitude is your primary pitch."

The approach didn't go smoothly. As he rolled out of the procedure turn, the trainee started descending to the MDA before intercepting the inbound course, which prompted an admonition from the instructor Another problem was introduced as the instructor pulled the circuit breakers for the gear lights and the flaps. He reset both breakers, though, as soon as the trainee identified the failures.

Adequate altitude control was still plaguing the trainee as he flew the inbound course. "I'm getting all disoriented here," was his comment. As he continued the approach, the instructor reminded him about their altitude three times so as not to bust the MDA.

The crew made a full-stop landing and paused on the ground for a few minutes with the engines running while they reviewed the approach. "On the partial panel," said the trainee, "all I can say is that it's been years."

The instructor responded, "Just fly the airplane first...if you're too low, first stop from getting any lower and then climb back up...it's better than trying to do everything at once."

Their debriefing complete, the crew took off. During climb-out, the instructor simulated a failure of the left engine by reducing power. He restored power 30 seconds later after the trainee followed the checklist and correctly identified the failed engine.

VOR Approach Next
They then briefed and set up for the VOR Runway 28 (see VOR chart).

At this point, they were about seven miles south-southwest of the VOR, proceeding inbound at 2500 feet. The instructor played the roles of both copilot and ATC:

"Maintain two-point-five till established. cleared for the approach."
"Okay," replied the trainee, "have a failure on the attitude indicator."

The instructor acknowledged, having once again pulled the circuit breaker for the AI as well as the flaps. Shortly thereafter, the trainee captain also identified the inoperative flaps. The instructor then reset the breaker for the flaps, but not the AI.

As they crossed the VOR, the instructor reminded the trainee to be "relatively aggressive about intercepting the outbound course." The trainee acknowledged, however, one minute later the instructor admonished him for using only a five-degree intercept toward the radial. The radar ground track shows that they were north of the radial before starting the procedure turn.

After turning to the procedure turn heading of 49 degrees, the trainee told the instructor to time for one minute. The instructor acknowledged and reduced power on the right engine. After identifying the failed engine, the crew responsively read the checklist procedure for feathering an engine, but actually kept the right engine at flight idle. They were halfway through the procedure turn and at 1,900 feet. (The procedure turn altitude at the time of the accident was 1,700 feet. instead of 1,500 feet as indicated on the chart.)

After one minute, the trainee turned right to complete the procedure turn and briefed the instructor regarding the airspeeds for a single-engine approach and lending. As he completed the procedure turn, the trainee asked:

"What altitude am I good down to?"
Then, seconds later, "Oh ####." but didn't elaborate about the problem.

He must have had difficulty controlling the airplane, since the instructor interjected:

"Stop one thing at a time. You're in a bad situation so correct one thing first."

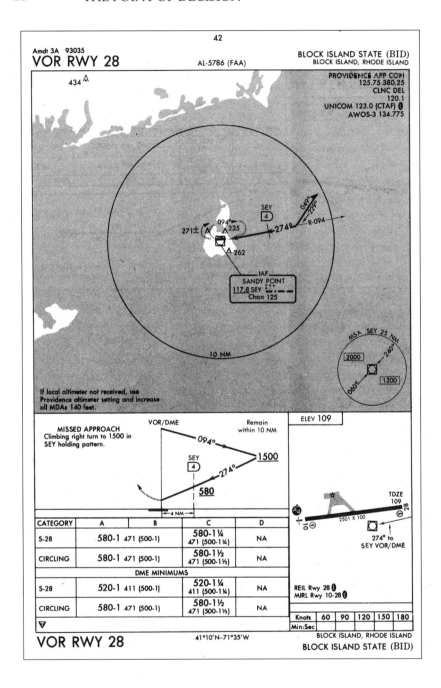

42

Amdt 3A 93035

VOR RWY 28

AL-5786 (FAA)

BLOCK ISLAND STATE (BID)
BLOCK ISLAND, RHODE ISLAND

PROVIDENCE APP CON
125.75 380.25
CLNC DEL
120.1
UNICOM 123.0 (CTAF) ◐
AWOS-3 134.775

If local altimeter not received, use
Providence altimeter setting and increase
all MDAs 140 feet.

MISSED APPROACH
Climbing right turn to 1500 in
SEY holding pattern.

ELEV 109

CATEGORY	A	B	C	D
S-28	580-1 471 (500-1)		580-1¼ 471 (500-1¼)	NA
CIRCLING	580-1 471 (500-1)		580-1½ 471 (500-1½)	NA
DME MINIMUMS				
S-28	520-1 411 (500-1)		520-1¼ 411 (500-1¼)	NA
CIRCLING	580-1 471 (500-1)		580-1½ 471 (500-1½)	NA

REIL Rwy 28 ◐
MIRL Rwy 10-28 ◐

TDZE 109

274° to
SEY VOR/DME

2501 X 100

Knots	60	90	120	150	180
Min:Sec					

VOR RWY 28

41°10′N–71°35′W

BLOCK ISLAND, RHODE ISLAND
BLOCK ISLAND STATE (BID)

There It Is

Evidently, the situation didn't improve and seven seconds later the trainee asked:

"Your airplane?"
"No, take it." replied the instructor.

That's it, right there. The student has hit that point of decision, where he knows he's actually lost command of the airplane. Unfortunately, the instructor hasn't realized the same thing. The situation was going rapidly out of control. The instructor tried to get the trainee-captain to stabilize the airplane:

"Get the bank...power to idle...what are you doing that for?...all right."

Those were the last words before the airplane crashed and sank in water 120 feet deep.

Investigators believed the airplane continued in a right descending turn from the point of the last radar return until it hit the water. Although they couldn't positively determine the airplane's attitude when it hit the water, investigators believed the airplane was inverted when it went in. The pilots were never found and only 50 percent of the airplane was recovered. When examining the wreckage, investigators found the gear extended and the flaps at 8° (approach setting).

Instructional Methods

The pilot's and co-pilot's gyros in the Beech 1900 are powered from separate sources: the pilot's gyros are electrically powered, while the co-pilot's are vacuum powered. Company pilots told investigators that the instructor didn't like practicing partial panel. but it was required by the training manual. During night training, the instructor usually turned down the in instrument lights on his side of the panel so the left-seat pilot couldn't peek at the right side when partial panel.

The commuter was rapidly expanding and operating three different types of airplanes. Most of the company's flight training was conducted at night, when more airplanes were available after daytime revenue operations. No one was specifically in charge of the Beech 1900 training program, and no one was assigned to monitor and standardize instructional methods.

In its report, NTSB stated:

"Although it appears none of the company's operations specifications or operating policies and procedures were disregarded by the IP [instructor pilot] who was involved in the accident, the Safety Board believes that considerably more attention and communication from management was needed to assure adherence to standard instructional methods and to flight safety."

Simulator Not Fully Utilized

At the time of the accident, the commuter was using a BE-1900 flight simulator at Flight Safety for type-rating and ATP certificate checks. However. following the accident, the commuter contracted with Flight Safety to conduct the majority of its BE-1900 training in the simulator.

Every conscientious pilot wants to simulate emergencies in his/her airplane to experience the look and feel of the emergency in order to prepare for the real thing. However, some emergencies or combinations of emergencies should be practiced in the safety of a simulator or ground training device. While you might not get the precise feel of your airplane, you'll still develop the basic skills of instrument scan, interpretation, aircraft control and executing emergency procedures. Most importantly, you'll learn how to recognize that things are getting out of hand before they do.

As he flew both approaches. the trainee-captain quickly recognized and properly responded to every system failure induced by the instructor. His Achilles' heel, however, was controlling the airplane under partial panel. When the trainee was still having aircraft control problems during the second approach, a better instructional strategy would have been to concentrate on this area alone before introducing multiple emergencies.

You can't fix someone's problems with the fundamental skills of cross-check, interpretation and control by merely talking them through it. Once these skills have deteriorated, it takes practice to get them up to snuff. It's futile to continue other training until proficiency in this area is regained.

Instructor Disoriented?

The instructor must have lost altitude awareness as he calmly tried to talk the trainee through an unusual attitude recovery. Even though the sky was clear that night, there was no moon. The resulting "black hole" effect while maneuvering over the water demanded constant altitude awareness. This black hole or featureless terrain illusion can deceive you into believing you're higher than you actually are.

In a discussion about a "false horizon," the AIM warns:

"Sloping cloud formations, an obscured horizon, a dark scene spread with ground lights and stars, and certain geometric patterns of ground light can cre ate illusions of not being aligned correctly with the actual horizon. The disoriented pilot will place the aircraft in a dangerous attitude."

NTSB noted the instructor's voice didn't reflect any stress or excitement before the crash. Did the instructor suffer spatial disorientation? It isn't clear from the recording. Since he had fully functioning gyros on his side, you'd think he would have assumed control to recover when the trainee got confused beyond recovery. In its findings, NTSB stated:

"Contributing to the accident was the instructor pilot's exercise of poor judgment in establishing a flight situation and airplane configuration conducive to spatial disorientation that afforded the pilots little or no margin for error."

A night operation in good weather often requires the same instrument discipline as if you were in the clouds. Under these circumstances, don't practice any maneuvers while VFR that you wouldn't practice in the clouds.

Missed Opportunity

We'd argue that this crash would not have happened had the instructor taken control the moment the trainee asked him to. The trainee-captain knew that the approach was blown and that he was no longer in control.

We don't mean to suggest that flight instructors automatically assume control every time a student gets flustered: Many of the most valuable lessons are learned when a student proves to him or herself that they really can get out of a sticky situation. But, an instructor must stay a couple of steps ahead, both of the student and of the airplane. That's what allows them to make life-saving decisions in time.

The Domino Effect

T his is the tale of a fuel exhaustion accident. It's like all fuel exhaustion accidents in that the pilot didn't count on running out of fuel...but circumstances dictated otherwise.

This accident report was prepared by editor Russ Lawton, who is also an ATP/CFII, and co-author of judgment training manuals for FAA. Unlike the previous two case histories, we'll follow up on this one with a detailed analysis and some decision-making tools.

Thinking Through a Safe Flight

"Plan your flight and fly your plan" is an axiom that has served aviation well. The importance of thorough preflight planning cannot be overemphasized. But to minimize the risks of flying, a pilot must go beyond merely "flying the plan." It's rare when situations encountered en route don't require the plan to either be changed or scrapped in favor of safer alternatives.

Detecting and responding to change requires sound decision-making. A good plan followed by good headwork can do much to minimize risk. But, as the following accident scenario shows, the results of poor planning and decision-making can be tragic.

As you read along, try to pick out the points where decisions either weren't made or were not made properly. You might want to make some notes, because we're going to follow up later in the chapter with a description of an organized method for decision-making and analyze how the method might have prevented this accident.

Florida-Bound

It was 7 o'clock on a Friday evening in March. A non-instrument-rated private pilot, his wife and an instrument-rated flight instructor departed Zelienople, Pa. on a VFR flight to Clearwater, Fla. A fuel stop was planned for Raleigh, N.C.

The private pilot flew from the left seat, with the flight instructor next to him and his wife in the back seat of the rented Cessna 172L. The Skyhawk had 4.7 hours' endurance at 75 percent power and 5,000 feet with the mixture properly leaned. At 82 percent power, endurance was 4.2 hours. Neither figure includes the fuel needed for taxi, takeoff, descent and landing.

Remember those endurance numbers; they were critical in the events that followed.

Change in the Weather

Weather was VFR along the first 100 miles of the route, but there were warning signs that it would change. Morgantown, W.Va. was reporting 5,000 broken and 15 miles' visibility, temperature 58/dew point 39, and "pressure falling rapidly."

Martinsburg, 94 miles east, was reporting 1,000 scattered, 2,500 overcast and 7 miles' visibility, temperature 39/dew point 36, and "ridge top obscured west."

The flight instructor got the current conditions before takeoff but didn't ask for the synoptic situation, winds aloft, sigmets and airmets. As a result, the pilots had no knowledge of a sigmet for their entire route for locally severe turbulence. Nor did the pilots know about an airmet warning of occasional moderate mixed icing in clouds and precipitation above the freezing level.

By 8:30 p.m., over Morgantown (see the accompanying chart) at 5,500 feet, they realized their progress was slower than expected—a lot slower. It took 90 minutes to travel 76 nm. Their groundspeed was only 51 knots.

The instructor called Morgantown FSS and asked for the Raleigh weather. He was told that there was a stationary front in the area, with low ceilings and poor visibility. He told Flight Service they would stop in Richmond, instead of Raleigh, but didn't ask for the winds aloft.

From Morgantown, they planned to fly direct to Kessel Vortac, direct to Linden Vortac (43 miles southeast), then direct to Richmond.

Unaware of the 60-knot crosswind, the pilot had difficulty tracking Morgantown's 121-degree radial to Linden, and the aircraft began deviating far to the north.

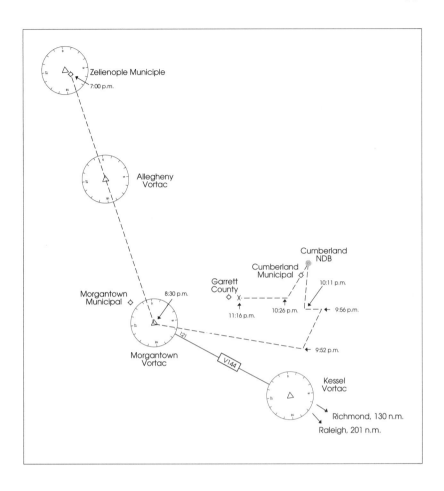

Confusion

About 50 miles southeast of Morgantown, the Skyhawk entered the clouds and the instructor took control. He soon became confused about his position and, at 9:43 p.m., called Washington Center and said, "We're not quite sure where we're at and wonder if you could help us out?"

The controller identified the aircraft on his radar display and determined that the instructor's VOR indications were correct. At this point, the instructor said they had one hour of fuel remaining.

The controller replied, "N4368Q, you're in radar contact, 10 miles north and east of the Kessel VOR. Say your intentions." The time was 9:52 p.m.

"Where can we get down, sir?" the instructor asked. The controller checked weather at Washington-Dulles, Martinsburg and Harrisburg, Pa. All were below minimums, but Hagerstown, Md. was reporting 800 overcast, with 2-1/2 miles' visibility. The instructor decided to go to Hagerstown, 53 miles to the northeast.

Turn Around?

Two minutes later, the controller called, "68Q, Morgantown is carrying 4,500 broken with 10 miles, if you'd like to go back towards Morgantown."

"Maybe that'd be better yet. Let's go back there," replied the instructor. He accepted a heading of 270 degrees for vectors to Morgantown. The aircraft was handed off to Cleveland Center at 10:04 p.m., and the following conversation ensued.

Center: "4368Q, turn left to a heading of 260."

68Q: "260, 4368Q."

Center: "I'm gonna vector you over to Garrett County Airport, which is at your 12 o'clock position, 25 miles. It's a lighted field and...may be able to make it in there."

68Q: "Okay, roger, 4368Q."

Center: "And 4368Q, in about another 10 miles, I can start you down. If I start you down now, I'll lose you on radar."

68Q: "Okay, we'll (unintelligible) whenever you're ready."

Center: "Roger, you say about an hour's fuel left?"

68Q: "(Unintelligible) probably about 45 minutes."

Center: "Roger."

Night NDB Approach

It was 10:10 p.m. N68Q was seven miles south of Cumberland and 25 miles east of Garrett County Airport. The controller asked the instructor if he could fly the NDB approach into Cumberland if the controller read the approach procedure to him. The instructor agreed. The Cumberland weather was given as 2,500 overcast and five miles' visibility.

When the instructor reported receiving the Cumberland NDB, the controller said, "You can proceed out on the 316-degree radial. Your inbound radial is 208 degrees." We rejoin the conversation as 68Q is over the NDB and inbound to the field.

Center: "68Q, did you receive?" (No response). "4368Q, Cleveland." (No response). "4368Q, if you receive Cleveland Center, the Cumberland Airport is at 12 o'clock, two miles."

68Q: "4368Q, we have the beacon, I...the squawk turned on. I didn't...the last transmission from you."

Center: "68Q, roger, if you have the field in sight, you are cleared to land."

68Q: "We're still 8,000 feet. Can we start down now?"

Center: "That is correct. I'm going to lose you on frequency. You are cleared to land. You do say you have the airport in sight?"

68Q: "We don't. I'm at 8,000 feet with an overcast beneath me."

Center: "68Q, roger, you are cleared to circle to land at the Cumberland Airport."

68Q: "Roger, cleared to circle to land at the Cumberland Airport."

Center: "68Q, that is correct. Now I'm going to lose you on Center frequency here. Cancel with Martinsburg Radio. Call Martinsburg Radio with your ground time."

Center (background conversation): "He most certainly did have it in sight. He had the rotating beacon in sight."

Center: "68Q, you receive Cleveland?"

68Q: "Yeah, we gotcha."

Center: "Roger, you are two miles north of the field now."

68Q: "We're circling here trying to descend to get it down. I'm still coming out of 7,000 descending. We just passed the beacon."

Center: "68Q, roger, but you do still have the field in sight?" (No response). "68Q, you still hear Cleveland?"

68Q: "Yeah."

Missed Approach

As 68Q descended slowly from 7,000 feet, the controller asked, "You will be turning south toward the field?" The instructor replied that he was still trying to lose altitude and asked the airport's position relative to the NDB. "The airport is two miles southwest of the beacon," the controller answered.

At 10:20, the controller told the pilot, "Cross the beacon inbound at 3,000 feet on heading 208." Then, radio contact was lost for awhile.

The instructor would later recall that he had crossed the NDB at 3,000 feet on a heading of 208. He was in heavy rain and couldn't see the ground. He remembered the reported ceiling and descended to 2,500 feet. He could see lights through the clouds but couldn't identify anything.

He then descended to 2,000 feet, where he could see the tops of houses and other objects but not the airport. He circled once in an unsuccessful attempt to find the airport, which is flanked by high ridges, then executed a missed approach.

Climbing on a southwest heading, the instructor called Cleveland Center to report that he had missed the approach due to low ceilings and heavy rain. He was cleared to 5,000 feet on a heading of 200 degrees.

At 10:36, 68Q was told to turn to 270 degrees for Morgantown and was asked to report the amount of fuel remaining. The instructor responded that he had 30 minutes left.

Eight minutes later, the controller said, "The rain showers seem to have passed by the Cumberland Airport. Would you like to try another approach? With the amount of fuel you have there and the winds, it's going to be rather close to Morgantown." The instructor declined.

Time Runs Out

At 10:57 p.m., the instructor said he had the rotating beacon at Garrett County Airport in sight. The controller gave him a heading to the airport and told him to stay at 5,000 feet until five miles from the airport. The following conversation took place about 15 minutes later:

Center: "68Q, I have lost you on radar 2.5 miles northeast of the field."

68Q: "Roger, 68Q. We have the (unintelligible) runway."

Center: "68Q, roger. You can stand by with the airport personnel on 122.8 now for your down time."

68Q: "122.8, thank you very much now. We appreciate everything you've done."

The instructor recalled that he switched to 122.8 and made one transmission when his tanks ran dry and the engine lost power. He found an open field to land in, but during landing roll, the aircraft struck a line of trees and crashed two miles from the end of the runway. The time was 11:16 p.m.

The private pilot was killed by the impact. His wife and the instructor were seriously injured, but survived.

What Went Wrong?

A close examination of the accident reveals that inadequate preflight planning, poor decision-making and some overly helpful controllers played significant roles.

When asked why he hadn't prepared a flight log for the trip, the instructor said it wasn't necessary because he had a "pretty good idea" of what his fuel and time estimates should be. Though a thorough weather briefing was in order, the instructor had checked only current conditions. Had he known about the strong winds aloft or the airmet and sigmet, they might have canceled the flight.

By the time the aircraft reached Morgantown, a third of its fuel had been used up. Though the instructor realized that they could not reach Raleigh and changed their destination to Richmond, about 174 nm from

Morgantown, he wasn't fully aware of just how slowly the trip was progressing. Had he checked his ground speed, he would have known that even Richmond wasn't feasible.

When the instructor had difficulty tracking the VOR radial, he didn't believe the CDI indications. "I could not get back to the right and get on course," he said. At no time did he consider that he had a 60-knot direct crosswind from the right.

His circling only worsened the fuel situation. He also pressed on into the clouds without an IFR clearance. At this point, the aircraft had been airborne for 2 hours and 25 minutes and had traveled only 140 nm.

After contacting ATC and learning that the weather at nearby airports was below minimums, the instructor decided to return to Morgantown—a good decision. But after that, like too many pilots in a sticky situation, he put all of his eggs into ATC's basket.

He told Cleveland Center he had one hour's fuel remaining. Trying to be helpful, the controller told 68Q that he would provide vectors to Garrett County, since it was closer than Morgantown. The instructor agreed.

In another attempt to be helpful, the controller told the pilot that the ceiling at Cumberland was 2,500 feet and asked if he would like to try the NDB approach. Unfortunately, the controller's report was third-hand information from an aircraft that had just departed Cumberland. The aircraft actually had reported the ceiling as 2,700 feet MSL, which meant that it was actually at 1,900 feet over the mountainous airport.

Compounding the situation was a misunderstanding between the controller and the pilot during the approach. When the instructor reported that he had the "beacon," he meant the Cumberland NDB. The controller, thinking the instructor meant the airport rotating beacon, stopped reading him the approach.

As a result, the pilot didn't know the minimum descent altitude and actually descended below the MDA and circled in the vicinity of some very rough terrain while trying to spot the airport.

After the missed approach, the instructor finally took command of the situation by asking for guidance to Garrett County, but it was too late. The consequences of poor planning and decision-making had caught up with the flight.

A Review

Now, let's take another look at the same accident and see how an organized approach to decision-making might have led to a better outcome.

Let's begin by reviewing the major details of the ill-fated flight. Night had already fallen when the trio took off from their home base in Pennsylvania to fly to Florida. A fuel stop was planned in North Carolina. The flight instructor had obtained only a sketchy preflight weather briefing. As a result, the pilots did not know of a sigmet for severe turbulence or of very strong winds aloft.

They were more than an hour and a half into the flight when they realized their ground speed was very slow—at one point, averaging only 51 knots. After contacting an FSS for some weather information, they decided to land at Richmond, rather than Raleigh, for fuel. But they still hadn't asked about winds aloft, and their decision showed that they remained ignorant about the strength and direction of the winds that night. Even Richmond was out of reach.

Lack of knowledge about the winds began causing gross navigational errors and confusion, and the Skyhawk began deviating far north of course. To make things worse, the pilots pressed the VFR flight into instrument conditions. At this point, they contacted ATC for help.

Declaring only an hour's fuel remaining, the pilots proceeded to put all their eggs in ATC's basket, heading first for Hagerstown, Md., which was above IFR minimums, then Morgantown, W.Va., which had VMC, then to Garrett County, Md., which was the closest airport. After all that, the pilots agreed to the controller's suggestion to proceed to Cumberland and shoot an NDB approach, even though they did not have the approach plate and apparently did not know that the airport is flanked by mountains (a bad place for a nonprecision approach, especially an off-airport NDB).

A communications miscue then occurred when the instructor, who had taken over control of the Skyhawk from the private pilot, reported that he had the beacon, meaning the NDB. The controller thought he meant the airport rotating beacon and stopped reading him the approach procedures, including the minimum descent altitude. The instructor then proceeded to circle below the MDA in a vain attempt to spot the airport.

The flight could easily have ended there, but the Skyhawk miraculously avoided the hills. The instructor finally climbed out of there and headed back toward Morgantown. Here, he made a good decision—not to try another NDB approach to Cumberland. On the way to Morgantown, he spotted the rotating beacon at Garrett County, but the Skyhawk did not have enough fuel left and crashed into trees two miles from the runway.

Six-Step Process

In the early 1970s, an organized process for decision-making was created by Ludwig Benner, Jr., an engineer and safety consultant in Washington, D.C. The process, called DECIDE, has been used to train more than 200,000 emergency-response personnel over the years with impressive results. There hasn't been a single fatality among these people since they received the training.

A training program for pilots based on the DECIDE model was developed in 1985 by Ludwig Benner, safety consultant Rick Clarke and myself at the AOPA Air Safety Foundation and tested with good results at Ohio State University. The simulator tests at Ohio State showed the model is readily adaptable for pilots and, as we shall discuss later in this report, could possibly have prevented the accident.

DECIDE is an acronym for a six-step decision-making model that can be learned and practiced. The six steps are to:

1. Detect change.
2. Estimate the need to react.
3. Choose the desired outcome for the flight.
4. Identify successful actions to control the change.
5. Do something positive to adapt to the change.
6. Evaluate the effects of your actions.

The first step, *Detect*, involves noticing either that an unexpected change has occurred or that an expected or desired change has not occurred. During preflight, the pilots of the Skyhawk (68Q) eliminated their chance of detecting change by passing up a complete weather briefing. As a result, they launched without knowing critical information about unusually strong winds aloft that would prevent the Skyhawk from reaching its planned fuel stop.

This is common in many accidents, where pilots decide to make a trip and either fail to seek out or ignore information that doesn't support their decision to go.

Safety First

The pilots did detect, albeit very late, an unexpected change when they reached Morgantown and found that their progress was slower than expected. They also appear to have followed the next step in the DECIDE process and evaluated the change and *Estimated* how it could affect the outcome of the flight. The pilots determined that their ground speed would make it impossible to reach their first stop in Raleigh as planned.

The third step in the process—*Choosing* the desired outcome—really is just a reminder. The choice always should be a safe landing, even if it must be at an airport other than the planned destination. Reminding yourself of the desired outcome helps you in the fourth step, which is to *Identify* alternatives that will accommodate a safe landing. We assume the pilots of 68Q chose a safe outcome because of their decision to obtain weather information from Flight Service.

In the fifth step, you *Do* something that adapts to the change after considering all of the alternatives. This is where the decision-making process broke down for the pilots of 68Q. When they called Flight Service, they asked only for the Raleigh weather, robbing themselves once again of an opportunity to know what they were up against.

They didn't request the winds aloft or conditions en route, which further illustrates their determination to make it to Florida. If they had asked, they would have discovered a newly issued airmet and sigmet for IFR conditions and turbulence along their route.

The pilots decided to switch their fuel stop to Richmond instead of Raleigh. A simple ground speed calculation would have revealed that this decision was flawed—that they couldn't make it to Richmond, either.

Follow Up

The final step in the process requires that you *Evaluate* the effectiveness of your actions. As we've already seen, the pilots did not assess their decision to press on to Richmond.

It's not enough to take action in response to a problem. You must constantly review the DECIDE process to figure out if further action is necessary. Each change that occurs should trigger the process and force you to review the flight.

The next change occurred when they entered the clouds 50 miles southeast of Morgantown. Apparently, their decision-making followed the first five steps of DECIDE since the flight instructor took control of the airplane in response to this change. But he ignored the last step in the process, in which he should have evaluated the effectiveness of his response. The prudent action would have been to make a 180-degree turn and return to VFR conditions. Instead, he continued flying in the clouds without an IFR clearance, and the problems quickly became compounded.

The instructor recognized his inability to track the radial southeast of the Kessel Vortac as a change. But his decision-making again proved faulty when, rather than identifying the need for crosswind correction, he suspected the Skyhawk's VOR equipment was malfunctioning and called ATC for assistance. (Not that asking for help is a bad decision. It is just that the pilot should have been able to solve the navigational problem by himself. If he'd used an organized approach to decision-making, he might have been able to do so.)

Though he recognized the need to respond to the change, he failed to review his actions. The CFI didn't fully confess their predicament when he called Washington Center and said, "We need a little assistance here. We're not quite sure where we're at and wonder if you could help us out?" He never admitted they were in the clouds.

Effects of Stress

The situation continued to deteriorate. It was dark. They were in the clouds without an instrument clearance. They were being bounced by moderate turbulence, and the fuel supply was dwindling. Stress in the cockpit must have been high, and stress overload can inhibit the ability to think clearly and make good decisions unless an organized approach is used.

From this point, the CFI cut short his decision-making and merely reacted to change. He told ATC, "We'd like to get down." In other words, he was saying, "I need you to tell me where I can land." Because he didn't have an alternate plan or knowledge of the weather at other airports, the instructor transferred decision-making to the controller. ATC can be a great backup, but a pilot should never require a controller to make his or her decisions.

The DECIDE process isn't for firefighters and pilots, only. It works for anyone, including controllers. After being told that 68Q had one hour of fuel remaining and wanted to land, the controller checked the weather at several airports and found that Hagerstown was above IFR minimums. He suggested a landing there and the instructor immediately agreed. The instructor's high stress was reflected in his hasty response, since he didn't calculate whether he had enough fuel to reach Hagerstown.

The controller became more involved in making decisions for the instructor. After providing a vector to Hagerstown (where the weather was 800 and 2-1/2), the controller suggested a heading to Morgantown, which had a 4,500-foot ceiling and 10 miles' visibility. Again, the instructor hastily agreed. The controller wasn't sure if this would work either, but it seemed like a good suggestion.

Blind Faith

While on the vector to Morgantown, 68Q was handed off to Cleveland Center, where another controller got involved in the decision-making process. The Cleveland controller told (not asked) 68Q that he would provide vectors to Garrett County Airport. The instructor went along.

Both center controllers, trying to be helpful, were doing more than making decisions for 68Q. They were introducing changes at an alarming rate, and the instructor never seemed to evaluate each change. Instead, he followed them as they were issued.

The instructor was using the "any port in a storm" method of decision-making. His knee-jerk reaction of bouncing from one suggestion to the next is known among human factors researchers as "change control." With this method, you react to change by using whatever method seems to work, without assessing your response against the desired outcome of the flight—a safe landing.

Proper use of the DECIDE process requires that you project possible responses to change on the outcome of the flight. This forces you to think ahead and to answer the question, "Will my response lead to a safe outcome for this flight?" If the answer is no, you must choose an alternative that assures safety.

Stress or panic can lead you to short-circuit the process and into the change control mode. The flight instructor continued to make decisions in this manner until his unsuccessful approach at Cumberland.

Taking Control

After the missed approach at Cumberland, the controller suggested another attempt. The instructor declined after evaluating the risks involved. He was finally assessing his options realistically, albeit too late.

His decision to attempt a landing at Garrett County was good but would have been much better had he stuck with that decision before the approach to Cumberland. The extra time he took for the approach would have provided enough fuel to reach Garrett County. Instead, the tanks ran dry two miles short of the runway.

Using the DECIDE process won't tell you what decision to make, but it does force you to think about and project the outcome of the flight. As a result, it can be used by pilots of all experience levels.

For example, faced with the same situation as 68Q, a 200-hour pilot might not know many solutions for a safe outcome due to limited experience. However, if that pilot chooses a course of action that he or she knows will lead to safety, the process has accomplished its purpose. A 5,000-hour pilot, on the other hand, will probably be able to think of more options and can use the same process to choose the one that best assures a safe outcome.

• Section Two •

Risk Management

IFR Safety
Strategies

The topic of risk management is a broad one. We can examine it from many angles, ranging from the purely theoretical (as in playing the "What If?" game, e.g., "What if ATC gives me a clearance I don't think is safe?") to the utterly practical ("I have a head cold, and am not fit to fly at altitude.").

While the title of this book suggests that the important moment in managing risk is the one in which a decision is made, we must not forget that a whole series of events precedes that moment. In many cases, taking the correct approach before the fact can avert the very need to make a hasty decision. In other words, the background is important to the decisions you do make in the cockpit.

Contributor Bill Kelly, former naval aviator, Navy and Piper factory test pilot in addition to a pile of other ratings, is one of the more practical people we know. Here are some of his thoughts on managing risks when flying single-pilot IFR.

IFR Safety Strategies

Compared with many other professions and avocations, aviation is hazardous. And no matter how you cook it, analyzing the steps that led to someone else's misfortune is a mighty good learning method.

Believe it or not, the "average" GA pilot is not concerned much about safety and isn't interested in learning about managing the risks involved in flying.

We have got to use our heads, or we will just add to the "average" GA statistics—and we will forever be more dangerous flying our aircraft than driving our family cars.

But we don't have to be "average." We don't have to repeat the "average" pilot's mistakes. We don't have to fly "average" GA airplanes. We don't have to stumble into IFR weather on a VFR flight, arrive at our destination only to find un-landable weather or winds. We don't have to run out of fuel.

Once we accept the fact that flying a small airplane is relatively risky, we can take steps to manage the risks.

How? Not by quitting flying, I hope. After all, did you quit scuba diving or sell your skis just because those activities are a little risky? Did you trash your kids' bikes? No more skateboards for the little ones? Heck no. But I'll bet many of you have taken diving and skiing safety courses and insist the kids wear helmets and pads while cruising the concrete.

Fine Print

Your insurance company is involved in risk management, also. Read the fine print in your airplane owner's or rental policy. You'll find it isn't worth the paper it's printed on if you are shy on the training/experience requirements, if your medical isn't up to date, if the airplane isn't in compliance with inspection requirements.

Insurance companies don't want to do business with the "average" GA pilot. They want only good risks—or much bigger premiums. Same with your life and auto insurance.

A local pilot recently learned a lesson about risk. He had let his big, expensive, out-of-production STOL single sit outside for many months without flying. When he attempted to take the bird aloft, the engine quit right after takeoff. No injury, except to pride, but there was major structural damage to the sheet-metal fuselage.

Reason? Water in the fuel—lots of it. Sure, on some planes like this old STOL model, it's a pain to do a good sump draining. So, if you like taking chances, just assume there's no water in the fuel. One day you'll join the ranks of the "average" pilot.

A rental operator I know can't even buy hull coverage for his training fleet, and his liability premiums have gone sky-high. Reason: too many crunches. There was a seat slide on takeoff in a Cessna 172 with badly worn seat tracks, and fuel exhaustion in a light twin with known erroneous fuel gauging. This guy does not involve himself in risk management. But his insurance company does, and some customers have decided to manage their personal risks by not flying his airplanes anymore.

Asking For It

Recently, I got to fly in an older Aerostar. The owner knew his airplane pretty well, apparently. He was content to continue flying with an inoperative ammeter and fuel gauge. There were lots of comm problems, also. The control tower couldn't read us on either transmitter. One day this beautiful, neglected old Aerostar is going to rise up and bite its owner.

While we're on the subject of asking for trouble, how many of you small-plane drivers—especially you tail draggers—practice crosswind landings regularly? How about short-field landings and takeoffs?

And you multi-engine pilots: When was the last time you got some good dual instruction on engine-out procedures? When was the last time you took your AFM home and read it from cover to cover?

And you instrument-rated pilots: Do you really maintain *proficiency* or just currency, as defined by the six/six/six rule? Proficiency and currency are not the same. When was the last time you hired a CFII for some concentrated recurrency training?

Setting Limits

Several years ago, I tried to manage the risks for an instrument student. Call him Henry. After much agony, Henry finally passed the check ride. Except for some problems with ADF work, he did pretty good on the check ride. He was happy—until I advised him not to shoot an actual ILS. "Practice under the hood, to your heart's content," I said, "but only do the localizer approach in real goo."

Why such a limitation? Well, because Henry, just like most of us, doesn't stay proficient enough to be going down to a 200-foot decision height with a half mile visibility. Henry doesn't get enough practice to be able to smoothly fly both the localizer and glide slope needles and still have good control of attitude, heading and airspeed. But Henry can do a real good localizer approach—right on centerline, all the way. Sure, he has to level out at an MDA several hundred feet higher than DH—but considering his usual proficiency, it's a lot safer.

Safer for you and me, too. We are not professional pilots, most of us, flying instruments every day. Just because FAR 91 gives us a lot of leeway, doesn't mean that we have to take full advantage of bare VFR weather minimums or of instrument approach minimums or of the no-checkout-needed if already rated in a particular airplane "class."

Strapping Up

How about that shoulder harness? If you have one, you gotta use it: That's the law, now, as well as good common sense. As PIC, you have to make sure that your passengers wear all of their available restraints, too. Also, you are obligated to ensure that they know how to open the doors and emergency exits. The airlines do all of this. But, guess what? In about half of the general aviation accident reports I read, shoulder harnesses were available but were not used. Surviving passengers often recalled that they were never briefed on emergency egress from the cabin.

Poor pilots, you say? Incompetent? Should not be flying? Baloney: These are our "average" GA pilots, the guys who make our statistics look so bad in comparison to automobiles, buses, trains and airlines. And that old Aerostar I mentioned earlier is not too far from the "average" GA airplane—lots of little things wrong.

Don't wait for the FAA to make things better for GA. We've gone as far as we can go through enforcement and regulation. No amount of government regulation can weed out all of the "bad apples." It's up to individual pilots and owners, now. It's up to each of us to make ourselves better.

Getting There

The statistics show that the GA accident rate has been steadily improving over the past 15-odd years. We must be doing something right. Though the numbers provide some grounds for optimism, we all know there's plenty of room left for improvement.

The key is just to recognize that there will be limits to where and when you can fly. Weather imposes its own set of limits. There will be times when you have to leave the airplane tied down and go Greyhound, Amtrak, airlines or automobile.

If you use common sense and good judgment, if you recognize the inherent risks of flying through the air and try to manage them by taking extra care and being extra cautious—you can be many times more safe than the "average" GA pilot.

You don't have to be a high-time pilot. Experience helps, but I've flown with 100-hour beginners who were safer than some 5,000-hour types.

Hard-Headed Strategy

The idea of a single pilot flying "hard" instruments is controversial, and I have to admit that I have a few reservations, such as:

1. If I need an airline ticket, I'm happy to pay a few bucks extra to have two pilots up front. But, if I've bummed a ride on a corporate or private bird, and if the guy or gal in the left seat has good equipment and is proficient, then I'm happy to go with only a single pilot. Leave the restrictive rules for the revenue passenger-carrying airlines.

2. Whether I'm doing the flying solo or just riding in the back of a one-

pilot airplane, I'd just as soon stay away from the big, congested airline terminals—New York, Los Angeles, Chicago, etc. Even in good weather, most small airplanes just don't mix well with the big, fast jets. Also, there's just too much traffic at the busy terminals, and a solo pilot will be hard-pressed to handle flying, communications and map-reading, and still be able to keep a good visual lookout. But, I'm *not* advocating another FAA regulation restricting my access to such airports.

3. If I'm going to fly single-pilot IFR in real instrument weather, the airplane, itself, has to be *perfect*. I'll accept no little glitches in the engine(s), electrics, avionics, fuel gauges and other essential equipment. The flight instruments have to be good, and I want a full suite of avionics. In the past, I've accepted airplanes that were missing such items as an ADF, marker beacons or glide slope receiver. That sometimes left me stuck with shooting very nonprecision approaches to airports where instrument landing systems were the preferred arrival method.

I'm not overly concerned about having only one engine or a single alternator and vacuum pump. I'll tailor my route and personal en route and terminal weather minimums to what I figure I can handle "partial panel" or with a single nav/comm running only on battery power.

Those are my major concerns when it comes to single-pilot instrument flying. Now, let's get to some specifics on equipment, procedures and the use of personal minimums.

Autopilot Assist

Here's what I look for if I'm going to do the flying and what I recommend to others who venture into IMC (instrument meteorological conditions) on their own:

First, an autopilot. It has to have altitude-hold, if only to keep me free from an automatic violation for getting more than 300 feet off the assigned altitude. (Before the "snitch-patch" bored its way into ATC software, I was happy with an autopilot that could hold pitch attitude.)

A nav coupler would be nice, too, even if it's an "oldie" that will track a VOR or localizer but not a glide slope. A coupler can help keep a nonprecision approach precise while I'm busy looking for the airport, obstacles and other traffic below the clouds.

One of the best ILS approaches I ever made was with the help of an old Altimatic-(whatever) in a Cherokee Six. It coupled to the localizer and kept me right on centerline while I hand-flew the glide slope to minimums. (Of course, the approach would have been much easier had I been able to couple the glide slope, also.)

I know, a lot of "experts" recommend against using an autopilot during instrument approaches. They would rather do it all by themselves.

Well, I'm not an expert. I just don't stay *that* current or proficient. I would not feel safe today hand-flying an ILS to 200 feet with a half mile visibility without another pilot aboard. A good autopilot coupled to the localizer and glide slope can shoot a much more precise ILS than I can hand-fly.

Also, I *can* do what a human does best—that is, to monitor the autopilot's performance and the progression of the approach while keeping a lookout for the approach lights and runway.

Misplaced Trust

In my opinion, it's really asking a lot of a single pilot to fly a precision approach manually and be ready for the transition to a visual final and touchdown while double-checking the landing gear position, flap setting, boost pumps, power settings, etc.

But that autopilot is *not* to be trusted if you don't exercise it regularly and don't really know how to use it.

In fact, if you don't know the proper procedures for intercepting a localizer and glide slope, executing a go-around or disconnecting, you shouldn't use it.

While conducting BFRs and instrument currency checks, I'm often amazed to find pilots who have never completely read, or recently reviewed, the autopilot supplements in their flight manuals. They don't know the restrictions on VOR or localizer intercepts. They don't recall the criteria for getting a smooth glide slope intercept. They don't know exactly what happens when they push that "go-around" button.

I also find that too many pilots do not perform the pre-takeoff check procedures specified for their autopilots. Some don't even realize that these procedures are tucked away in the back of the AFM, in the "Supplements" section.

I recently helped troubleshoot a problem experienced in a corporate turboprop twin flown by a single pilot. The owner/passenger and the young pilot were considerably disturbed and badly scared by several violent "porpoises" in pitch attitude while on autopilot.

It didn't take long to discover that the pilot had never read the autopilot supplement in the AFM and had never performed the autopilot pre-takeoff checks. He didn't know that trying to override the autopilot in pitch would cause the electric trim to run in the opposite direction. He didn't know that depressing the electric trim switch on his control wheel would disconnect the autopilot or that holding the red button, next to the trim switch, would both disconnect the autopilot aileron and elevator servos and the elevator trim servo. He didn't even know where to find the autopilot and electric trim circuit breakers! Obviously, this pilot should not have been using his autopilot, even for VFR flying.

An autopilot *can* be an important aid to flying, but you have to know the operating procedures just as well as you know engine-failure and emergency gear extension procedures.

To summarize, here are my recommendations concerning autopilots:

1. Review your entire AFM autopilot supplement frequently.

2. Exercise that autopilot regularly. Make it part of your "six/six/six" currency requirements. Do at least one coupled approach for every two you hand-fly.

3. Have the autopilot checked and adjusted if it's not working perfectly.

4. Use your autopilot, but don't trust it. Keep an eye on its performance and how the approach is progressing.

Compass Calibration

Let's move from the sublime to the simple, now, and give some thought to the magnetic compass.

A majority of the airplanes flying single-pilot IFR probably do not have an electrically "slaved" DG (directional gyro), just a vacuum-driven DG to accompany the "whiskey" compass. It's likely that, in some of the airplanes, the wet compass is half-dry and the DG precesses horribly during flight and makes lots of noise after engine shutdown.

It's sort of difficult to achieve good navigation or accurate approaches when you don't have a good direction indicator. And it all starts with having a *good* and *accurate* magnetic compass.

A "flux-gate" in the tail cone or wing tip, which drives a slaved direction indicator, will probably hold its accuracy for many years. But that whiskey compass in or above the panel tends to slip off calibration over the years as parts of the airframe become magnetized or as panel equipment is changed.

Adjustment of a wet compass isn't difficult. The procedures are outlined in mechanic's handbooks. You can even calibrate your own magnetic compass and make a new deviation card with only the aid of a known runway heading. (Magnetic headings usually jibe with ILS final approach courses and sometimes are provided in the airport diagrams on approach charts.) To be absolutely legal, you will probably want an A&P mechanic to sign off any compass adjustments or install a new deviation card.

Take a look at your compass. What's the date on the deviation card? Can you read the compass corrections for each 30 degrees of magnetic heading, or has the ink faded from age? Maybe you have one of those fictitious initial factory deviation cards that shows zero error on all headings. *Get that compass checked!*

That original-equipment DG which makes grinding noises following engine shutdown probably also needs resetting every five minutes in flight. Sure, it's getting old. The bearings are worn. Therefore, the gyro precesses excessively. Get it overhauled, or buy a new one.

It's a good idea to realign the DG with the magnetic compass every time you roll out on the final approach course, and include the deviation error in your DG setting. Even a good DG will tend to precess during your maneuvering or procedure turns onto final. If you don't reset the DG on final approach, you may be flying an imaginary crosswind down final on a VOR, ILS or localizer approach. If it's an NDB approach, your flight path over the ground and obstacles will be off by the same amount as the heading indicator error!

Get a Headset

If you are going to fly single-pilot IFR, you just *have* to have a headset with a boom microphone and a push-to-talk button on the control yoke.

Personally, I'm not fond of having that band over my head and the pressure on my ears. The mike always seems to be trying to sneak up a nostril or tickle my chin. I'd much rather use the overhead speaker and a hand mike. But the discomfort is a lot better than having to search for the hand-held mike halfway down an approach (usually just when I need the right hand to make a throttle adjustment) or having to ask for a repeat of an ATC instruction because I didn't quite get all of the reception over the overhead speaker.

Lately, a lot of pilots have been installing intercom systems in their airplanes so that they can talk with their passengers without shouting. To tell the truth, I'm not a big fan of intercoms, especially when I'm the only pilot, there's IMC and we are on an approach. Usually, that's the time a passenger will choose to talk or sneeze—just as I'm trying to communicate with approach control, the tower or unicom.

Unless the person in the right front seat is a qualified pilot and we've worked out how we're going to share the communication/navigation/control tasks, I *don't* want to hear his comments, coughs or heavy breathing. For single-pilot IFR, I want a switch that cuts off the intercom system completely.

For sure, I don't want an intercom that needs continual adjustment of the squelch control to keep cockpit, engine and breathing noise out of the headset. I'd much prefer an intercom without a "hot" mike—one which doesn't allow intercom chatter without depressing a "talk" switch.

Perhaps, I'm being a bit picky, but I'm serious about avoiding any unnecessary distractions when I'm flying IFR all by myself.

If the previous owner has installed a stereo tape player in the airplane, I would have it rewired so that it plays only through the back-seat headphones. I don't need music or comedy tapes playing in the cockpit—*ever* (even VFR).

Recently, a locally based Beech 18 was refurbished with a six-speaker, megawatt stereo system. Even with the volume cranked up only halfway, the din through the woofers and tweeters is worse than a rock'n'roll nightclub and can drown out even full volume over the cockpit headsets. With its controls in the cabin area, it could be a dangerous distraction to the pilot.

Redundancy

Let's get back to the equipment I *do* want if I'm going to do much IFR flying, even with another pilot helping out.

I'd like to have dual alternators or generators. My primary reason for desiring two engines for any IFR flying is that I like the idea of having two electrical generating sources, as well as two vacuum pumps. But the majority of airplanes that qualify for single-pilot IFR operations have only one engine and only one alternator and air pump.

I don't want to see a new regulation that would require a backup alternator for IFR operations in single-engine airplanes (or old twins that came from the factory with only one installed), but I would be willing to spend the bucks for the biggest and best battery the airplane is allowed to carry. I'd also spring for routine battery checks and frequent replacement.

Airplane batteries don't last as long as auto batteries. If you fly only day VFR in "Old Bessie," that ancient chunk of lead-acid is probably OK, so long as it gets the engine started on a spring day. But it's *not* safe for IFR and night flying. Alone on the gauges, you *don't* want a weak battery if an alternator-failure emergency should occur as you approach Podunk in close-to-minimums conditions. It's hard enough even when you have a copilot to handle the load-shedding tasks required to keep a nav and comm running on battery power.

There are some backup vacuum pumps and gyro pressure sources available on the market, and every single-pump airplane that ventures into IMC should have one. But, again, I'm not advocating a new rule.

A nice feature found in many medium and large twins is two full instrument panels. That offers quite a bit of redundancy, especially for the gyro instruments. Unfortunately, some of the older two-panel airplanes run both attitude gyros and both directional gyros from a common vacuum or pressure system. Too, some have both electric turn coordinators powered by the same source.

You don't really need a full copilot's panel if you regularly fly alone. The second airspeed indicator, altimeter and vertical speed indicator may never be needed. But a backup attitude indicator is highly desirable, especially if it's driven by a different power source than the primary gyro.

My dream airplane for single-pilot IFR would have a backup attitude gyro close to my pilot's panel and powered electrically if the main gyros were vacuum or pressure driven. This would be a standard installation in most airliners and military airplanes. It probably wouldn't cost any more than that fancy loran receiver or RNAV system you don't really *have* to have, and, since it's an "auxiliary" instrument, installation can probably be field-approved with a Form 337.

Back to the Doghouse

I would also scrap the turn coordinator in my dream machine and replace it with a turn needle (now officially called a *turn and slip indicator*).

A turn needle shows only yaw rate and is little affected by the minor turbulence and wing rocks that drive many turn coordinators crazy. The turn coordinator gyro axis is tilted, so that it senses roll rate as well as yaw rate. Many turn coordinators are so poorly damped that wing rocks in turbulence cause the tiny simulated airplane to provide violent turn indications.

Also, during recovery from an unusual attitude—say, from a steep, descending left bank (i.e., a graveyard spiral)—as soon as you *start* to roll right to recover, the turn coordinator may indicate a right turn, even though the aircraft still is steeply banked to the left. The indicator, then, is showing more of the roll *rate* to the right than the continuing turn rate and bank to the left.

I've flown a lot of actual partial panel during cropduster overwater ferry flights using both types of indicators (but without an attitude indicator). Please believe me, it's much easier and *safer* with the old-fashioned turn needle. That's what the airliners, military planes and most of the big general aviation twins use.

In my opinion, turn coordinators should be outlawed. They certainly should not be allowed to be used as a backup in single-pilot, single-panel IFR operations.

Use Your Head

I still remember a hairy ILS to near-minimums when the Jepp book dropped off of my lap just as I intercepted the glide slope. Halfway down the final, I wanted to recheck decision height. When I finally located the book on the floor, I found that it had flipped to another page, and there wasn't enough light in the cockpit to retrieve the correct approach plate.

That's no way to fly single-pilot IFR.

So, one rule I've set for myself is to never start the final approach segment without having *memorized* the decision height or minimum descent altitude, nonprecision timing and the initial part of the missed approach procedure.

You have no business attempting an approach to anything near minimums if you have to look at the plate halfway down final!

You've got enough to do just to fly the airplane, stay within approach criteria and look for the runway. You do not have time to be reading books on final approach. (If your memory isn't that good, then you should always bring along a good copilot.) Also, do yourself a favor and buy a good approach chart holder (one that will hold an entire NOS book, if that's what you use).

Personal Minimums

The FAA establishes altitude and visibility minimums based on an aircraft's ground speed during an approach. Each aircraft is supposed to fit into one of five approach categories (A through E) conforming to a formula that multiplies stall speed (Vso, at max gross weight) by 1.3.

For those who only occasionally fly single-pilot IFR, let me propose a new category: SP (for single-pilot). Here are some minimums I suggest for Category SP approaches:

1. Use only the circling minimums for VOR, NDB, RNAV and back course approaches. If you know that you aren't really proficient, or if you haven't made that particular approach recently, raise the circling minimums by 200 feet and one mile. Don't even file to a destination that isn't forecast to be at least 500 feet and one mile better than the circling minimums.

2. Disregard published ILS minimums. Consider them as suitable only for "professional" pilots—the guys and gals who fly almost every day or night.

That's right, let the airline pilots and the single-pilot daredevils flying night cargo or bank checks have the low minimums. Use the ILS approach chart but ask for and *fly* the localizer approach. Time the approach from the final approach fix and level-off at the MDA (minimum descent altitude).

I see a lot of unsafe approaches by rusty private pilots who try to hand-fly a full ILS to published minimums. The job of coordinating basic attitude/heading flying, power settings, airspeed control and localizer tracking is about all that one of us "average GA pilots" can handle. Throw in accurate tracking of the glide slope for a manual approach, and overall performance goes to pot. It's almost instinctive to "chase" the glide slope indicator when you don't have a good panel scan. Then, everything else gets fouled up.

Rather than trying to nail the glide slope needle, concentrate your effort on chasing and narrowing localizer errors. Level off at the MDA and fly out the approach time. With the typical half-mile visibility minimum, you should be able to see the runway, not just the approach lights, with sufficient room remaining to make a visual descent to a reasonable touchdown point.

If you use this method, you won't be able to go as low as you could using the full ILS, but you will be less likely to add to the statistics on those who flew into the approach lights.

If you get near the destination and the latest weather observation indicates that you won't be able to land using localizer minimums, it's time to use that autopilot-coupled ILS approach that you should have been practicing.

Or, better yet, go to your alternate.

Practical Considerations

Several years ago, I was involved in the investigation of an accident involving a twin turboprop flown by a nonprofessional and not-too-current pilot. His preflight briefing and en route and terminal advisories all indicated that the ceiling and visibility at the destination were *way* below ILS minimums.

Before takeoff and when starting the approach, the pilot was heard to say, "We'll go down and take a look." Well, he "looked" himself— and his passenger—right into a power line and the approach lights.

Perhaps, the outcome would have been different if the person in the right seat had been a qualified "copilot" (the twin did have two full panels). Perhaps not. But, the outcome certainly *would* have been better if the pilot had limited himself to safer minimums and had not filed and launched to a destination with ceiling and visibility reported as impossibly low.

Let's be realistic and consider the following:

1. Most of us are *not* professionals. We don't fly enough or get enough instrument practice to really stay proficient.

2. We should not expose unsuspecting passengers to our lack of expertise. We should not try to fly in weather that we are not ready for. We especially should not shoot instrument approaches in bare-minimum weather conditions.

3. Without an assisting copilot and training in cockpit coordination, we are not as fully capable as a professional two-pilot crew, even with a good autopilot aboard.

4. Many of our airplanes either are not completely equipped, or the equipment is not in sufficient calibration for instrument flight to published minimums.

No Time for Tests

Single-pilot IFR is not a time for experimentation. Beyond the instrument training syllabus, there are a few things you need to know.

For instance, you have to know the flap, landing gear, pitch attitude and power settings for each phase of the takeoff, climb, approach and missed approach. You don't have time to experiment with power settings and flap extension angles.

(Don't extend the flaps any more than to the takeoff or approach setting until you need them for landing. Even then, maybe you don't really need full flaps.)

You also should know the proper pitch attitudes for takeoff, missed approach and, especially, final approach with the landing gear down and in about a 500-fpm rate of descent. You ought to be able to conduct the first 500 feet of climb on go-around without referring to your airspeed or vertical speed indicators. Use what you know to be the proper attitude and power settings. Again, you do not have time to experiment.

Sure, go ahead and fly your single-pilot IFR flights. Just temper your route and destination weather with your current capability and proficiency, and with the equipment in your airplane.

If you don't feel good about yourself or your airplane, hire a good instrument instructor for some additional training and equipment checks.

Before launching on a "hard instruments" flight, ask yourself: "Could I pass the instrument rating flight check, oral and written examinations *today*?" If the answer is no, maybe you had better limit yourself to entering the clouds no lower than 500 feet AGL on takeoff and VFR minimums at the destination.

A Proper
Attitude

M*aking good decisions, using good judgment, is something we like to think is intrinsic; that it's part of our character. "Me? I always make good, carefully reasoned decisions. I never put myself at risk."*

Sure, you don't.

Good judgment must be learned. And the basis of that is a good attitude. In this chapter, corporate pilot Brian Jacobson shares some thoughts on a pilot without one.

Poor Judgment is a Killer

He was a flight instructor and charter pilot with thousands of hours in the air. He had a poor attitude, though, and it showed.

True to his light-the-fires-and-go approach to flying, he once grabbed a flight bag for a night trip to Chicago, not bothering to check the contents. It was only after he got airborne in IFR weather conditions that he discovered he didn't have any en route charts, only approach plates.

That was a fix he got himself out of with a little help from ATC, and it's fortunate that he didn't have a communications failure.

But, this is the same guy I once watched from the ground as he circled 50 to 100 feet above the airport in a heavy snowstorm, well below the MDA (minimum descent altitude) for the instrument approach he supposedly was conducting.

His airplane was in a steep turn to the left when it went out of sight in the poor visibility. Just when I began to think that he surely must have crashed, I saw the airplane rolling out on the snow-covered runway.

There was nothing this pilot couldn't handle—or so he thought. He was a good pilot, to be sure, but he took too many chances.

One day, he was flying a load of passengers in a Cessna 402. He had to make several stops, the last being about 50 miles from our home airport. Just after takeoff, one of the engines (I don't remember which) lost power.

He feathered the propeller. Then, in spite of being in the traffic pattern at a controlled airport that was more than sufficient for an emergency landing, he flew the airplane home. The paying passengers were still on board.

His excuse was that he felt our mechanics would want to fix the engine, themselves, instead of having to farm the work out.

No, as far as I know, he hasn't killed himself or any of his passengers, yet.

Several years after that pilot's senseless single-engine cross-country, I saw an interview on network news following a major aircraft accident that occurred during a landing attempt with a thunderstorm nearby.

The reporter was talking to a witness, unfamiliar with aviation, who said, "I don't know why the control tower let him land. It was lightning over there, and the wind was blowing like crazy."

Making the Call

What that fellow didn't know is that the pilot-in-command of an aircraft, unlike the principal players in many other fields of endeavor, has the sole responsibility for determining what is safe and what isn't.

And, when the PIC makes a call, he or she is exercising judgment based on what is known about the weather, the aircraft, its load and many other factors that pertain to that particular flight.

Some pilots, like the one I mentioned above, are good "stick-and-rudder men," but, when it comes to making a decision, they err—and not on the side of safety.

With few exceptions, emergency situations don't develop instantaneously. Usually, they are the result of a series of actions or events that, had the pilot recognized or acted upon earlier, could have been prevented from developing in the first place.

In other words, to paraphrase the old saw, the use of good judgment by pilots can prevent many circumstances from getting to the point where superior skills may be needed to survive.

We all know that individual pilots, like airplanes, have limitations. Our experience level, mental attitude and physical condition on the day of the flight determine what those limits should be. So, theoretically, a pilot's personal minimums could vary from day to day. In reality, this is true.

I know a businessman, for example, who flies his own Baron most of the time. Yet, if he plans to use his airplane to go to a meeting at which he will be making a major presentation, he forgoes the left seat and hires a professional pilot to fly him and his staff.

That accomplishes two things for him. First, during the flight, he can conduct business. He can, for instance, make the final decisions on the presentation and discuss with his staff the role of each participant.

Secondly, it relieves him of the burden of making additional important decisions regarding the safe flight of the aircraft while his mind is really somewhere else.

This pilot's personal minimums mostly reflect his projected mental attitude on the day of a particular flight. He knows that he has other things to think about and doesn't want to take on the responsibility of flying the airplane, as well.

That, in my opinion, is excellent judgment on his part. He makes a critical decision regarding a planned flight long before he gets into the airplane.

Some emergencies are the result of a lack of judgment that occurs long before the pilot pushes the throttles forward to initiate the takeoff run. They occur when pilots fail to develop a proper and thorough plan.

These emergencies can easily be avoided. For example, a pilot who watches the weather deteriorate the day before a flight would be wise to make alternate arrangements for getting to his destination.

That way, if the conditions should prove to be marginal for his experience level when he checks the weather the next day, he will feel less pressure to make the flight. He already will have made arrangements to take an airliner, a train or a bus—or to postpone the flight for another day.

The quality of your preflight planning will have an influence on your decisions during the flight.

Good strategy will include consideration of a series of "what ifs" that could cover alternate landing sites in the event of a mechanical problem, landing early or overflying the original destination because the weather deteriorated earlier than forecast, or planning for more head wind than expected.

Should an emergency develop during the flight, all of the earlier planning you accomplished will help you make the decision on how to handle it.

A pilot who does little or no planning exposes himself to the risk of making critical decisions "on the fly" while trying to keep everything under control.

That type of workload is not necessary.

The idea is that a pilot has to control whatever events occur during a flight, rather than have the events control him and leave him behind the airplane, playing catch-up.

Behind the airplane is a dangerous place to be even when no emergency exists. If the workload includes some unforeseen incident that reduces the pilot's ability to fly his airplane, disaster could be the final result.

Good preflight planning will be like money in the bank for a pilot who finds himself in that situation.

Expect the Worst

Multi-pilot crews brief themselves on exactly what each person will do in the event an emergency or an abnormal situation occurs during certain phases of flight. For instance, they know what they must do if an engine fails on takeoff or if a missed approach becomes necessary.

A single pilot should do the same. Making decisions based on existing conditions *before* you begin the takeoff roll will relieve you of a tremendous mental workload if something unforeseen does occur.

For example, imagine that you are about to take off from an airport with a ceiling at 300 feet and visibility of one mile. The airport has only a VOR approach, and you know that the existing weather conditions are below the landing minimums for that approach. That means you couldn't come back if something happened right after takeoff.

Let's say you're fortunate to be flying a twin, which could provide more alternatives than a single-engine airplane should an engine fail on takeoff. But, let's also say that the airplane has two new engines that have only ten hours of flight time on them. They are yet to be broken in, and it is still possible that there is a defect in one of them.

You look at the area chart and find a major municipal airport nine miles away that has two ILS approaches. You decide that if any problem comes up immediately after takeoff or while you are in the terminal area, you will land there. You even pull out the approach plates for that airport, so that they will be handy just in case.

Chances are, nothing will happen, and you will continue on your way as planned. But, in the event that one of those new engines quits, your decision is already made. You won't have to do any on-the-spot planning. You'll be free to concentrate your attention on flying the airplane. You will feather the propeller on the errant engine and let Departure Control know what you are going to do.

Such a plan will decrease the workload tremendously and allow you to concentrate on keeping the aircraft in the air.

Avoid Temptation

Many pilots, like the one who descended below minimums and landed in that snowstorm, have problems making safe decisions concerning instrument approaches in bad weather.

If the approach plate says the MDA is 840 feet, that means you are not to descend below that until the airport or the runway you are to land on (or one of the other items listed in FAR 91.175) is in sight.

Yet, it is tempting, especially when you can see the ground directly below, to descend another 50 feet, then another 50 feet, trying to get below the clouds.

Too many pilot have flown their airplanes into the ground while doing exactly that. Poor judgment by the pilots-in-command, to be sure.

It is easy to come up with reasons why this type of accident happens. But, to the people who die in these accidents, and to those they leave behind, the explanations are nothing but excuses.

I know pilots who are determined to get to their destination at all costs. They hate to say no to a passenger. And they press ahead, either because they feel they can handle whatever conditions exist, they have busted minimums on that approach so often that they think they can get away with it again or they fear the loss of their passenger's respect if they don't complete the flight as scheduled.

That's why there is so much more to pilot judgment than simply making safe decisions. A robot could be programmed to react to any circumstance that can be expected to occur. But, what if something entirely unexpected should happen?

A good example is the engine failure that resulted in the severe control difficulties and eventual crash landing of the United DC-10 at Sioux City, Iowa several years ago.

According to the manufacturer of the airplane, the chances of that happening were too remote to consider extra shielding for hydraulic control lines running near the engine.

A robot's database would not have afforded the ability to cope with the total loss of primary control. But, the human mind found a way to make the airplane stay in the air until it reached the airport. Many of the passengers' and crew members' lives were saved as a result.

Internal Factors

So, we find humans exercising good judgment, as they did in the cockpit of the crippled DC-10, and bad judgment, as in the frequent willful descents below published approach minimums.

The ability of pilots to exercise good judgment is one reason why humans will always be necessary in aircraft cockpits, no matter what types of wizard automation should come along.

But, we must reduce the risk of making poor decisions.

The poor decisions which are made by pilots often result from a lack of planning, not enough familiarization with the aircraft, too little experience in the operation being undertaken and other factors that can be considered to be "external."

Pilots can learn to overcome this type of bad decision-making by planning their flights better, learning more about the airplanes they are to fly and gaining more experience.

But, at times, a pilot consciously makes a decision knowing he will be violating a rule or safe principle. He knows that he is accepting undue risk and that an accident could occur. Yet, he goes ahead anyway.

This type of willful decision is an "internal" matter that is much more difficult to solve than the external matters already discussed.

It is not always possible to tell in advance what kinds of decisions some pilots will make. The "hazardous attitudes" we've all heard about do not always show up during training and flight checks.

For example, a while ago, I received recurrent training at a well-known flight training facility. That school's focus was on the aircraft's systems and the pilot's ability to handle emergencies that might occur during a flight.

By simply learning and practicing the correct responses to the situations presented, a pilot could successfully complete the training.

During this type of training, the decisions a pilot makes in the flight simulator are based on actual emergencies that could occur in his everyday flying. Through exposure to simulator training once or twice a year, a pilot learns and practices procedures that lend themselves to good external decision-making in the event specific problems occur.

Status Quo

But, what about the pilot who harbors a hazardous attitude that results in poor internal judgment?

If he has a lack of respect for his training situation, he will simply go through the motions, showing the instructor that he can do the basics and that he possesses the required knowledge of the airplane's systems.

But, no matter what the instructor presents, when he gets back into the cockpit of his airplane, he will do things the way he has always done them. He will derive nothing from his training and just repeat the cycle time after time because it is required by his company or insurance carrier.

That type of attitude about safety is difficult for any instructor to recognize and even harder to correct.

In a recent accident that occurred in Georgia, the pilots of a corporate jet departed an airport VFR intending to get their clearance in the air. Weather conditions were marginal, and, upon contacting the local approach controller for their clearance, they were told to stand by.

The airplane struck a nearby mountain, killing all aboard.

A similar accident occurred in California, when another jet crew took off from an airport at night in VFR conditions and flew into a mountain that they never saw.

Should the results of these two flights suggest that pilots should never take off VFR, intending to get an IFR clearance in the air?

No. But, they do illustrate the potentially high risks involved in this type of operation and point out how poor decisions (in these cases, resulting from poor planning) can cost lives.

Evidence gathered after the two accidents showed that both crews should have known about the nearby high terrain and that, under the prevailing conditions, it would be difficult to see the mountains.

But, instead of delaying their passengers for a few minutes and calling for an IFR clearance on the telephone, they elected to take off VFR without a sound plan for terrain-avoidance. They inadvertently gambled that they would be able to avoid the mountains. They lost.

Resource Management

The airlines and some major corporate flight departments are placing increased emphasis on Cockpit Resource Management (CRM) training in an attempt to enhance safety by improving decision-making.

To some extent, this type of training has helped multi-pilot crews work together to make decisions while the pilot-in-command retains final responsibility for their implementation.

But, what about the lone general aviation pilot who, while flying the aircraft, must do all the brainstorming, as well?

Some aspects of CRM do apply to the single-pilot operator, but there are few pilots who are exposed to them on a regular basis. So, many of us just plod along, doing things as we have always done them.

So, what can the average general aviation pilot do to improve his decision-making?

One tactic is to reduce the need to make on-the-spot decisions as much as possible by increasing the quality of your preflight planning and activities.

For example, a good preflight inspection of your aircraft might uncover a system or component that is about to fail. By correcting the problem before takeoff, you will eliminate the need to make a decision following the loss of the system and after considering all the alternatives and consequences that it involves.

You must objectively evaluate your experience level and be certain that any flight you undertake will not put you in a position to make decisions that you are not qualified or able to make.

For example, a newly rated instrument pilot, whether he has weather-avoidance equipment or not, should decide on the ground whether the forecasts calling for thunderstorms along his route of flight could present problems beyond his ability to solve them.

Beyond that, there is the need for a continuous, thorough evaluation of your attitude toward flying and the risks you are willing to take to reach your destination.

A pilot who establishes personal minimums, and sticks to them, is not likely to have the types of problems with internal judgment that some pilots encounter so often.

For some people, flying an airplane simply requires an attitude that is different from the approach they take toward their daily lives. Those who can't make the adjustment may have problems with internal and external judgment, and decision-making.

While they, too, can limit their exposure to on-the-spot decision-making that generates poor results, it is more likely that these are the people we will read about in accident reports.

Maintaining Focus

W*e're actually making decisions all the time, most of which are unconscious. Do you answer a passenger's question, ignore it and listen to the controller more closely, or is it really more important at the moment to concentrate on your heading?*

While most instrument flying is routine, occasionally the workload piles up and it's all too easy for a pilot to start paying attention to the wrong thing. Keeping focused on what's important requires the pilot to raise that unconscious process a notch and think actively about the situation and what's needed next.

Here we have Brian Jacobson to share some experiences gained from his 12,000 hours in the cockpit.

Deadly Distractions

In many of the accidents we read about, a contributing factor is the pilot's failure to concentrate on flying the aircraft because he or she became distracted by some other event that was taking place in or around the cockpit and forgot to look outside the window or at the instrument panel to verify what the airplane was doing.

I believe that once a pilot's concentration becomes fixed on something other than flying the airplane, he is disoriented. Does that mean you should *not* pay any attention to other things that are happening inside and outside the cockpit? Of course not. But, you must never allow your primary duty of flying the airplane to lose its priority.

In many cases, pilots become distracted by emergency situations, *perceived* emergencies that really aren't emergencies or equipment or system failures or malfunctions. These distractions cause them to devote more time in attempting to correct the discrepancy than to flying the airplane. The majority of us flying general aviation aircraft operate single-pilot, and that means we have to be capable of dealing with whatever should occur during a flight by ourselves. Sometimes, we will have another pilot in the aircraft who can help sort out problems; but, even in that situation, you have to be careful, as we'll see later.

You would think that multi-pilot crews would have more luck dealing with distractions than pilots flying solo. But, that is not always the case. Sometimes, all the pilots get so involved with trying to troubleshoot a problem that no one pays any attention to what the airplane is doing. There have been fatal accidents resulting from this.

The ultimate cockpit distraction occurred a few years ago when a fellow employee attacked the crew of a FedEx DC-10 with weapons he smuggled aboard the freighter. The flight had departed Memphis for San Jose, Calif. and was climbing through 18,000 feet when the hitchhiking company flight engineer viciously attacked the three pilots. At one point, all three crewmen left the flight deck while subduing the attacker, and the airplane was left to fly on autopilot. The pilots got control of the situation, but all three, and the attacker, sustained injuries and required hospitalization.

Precious Time

Distractions can happen in any cockpit, from the simplest to the most complex, without warning. They are insidious because they may start out as something totally innocent—an engine gauge that isn't reading correctly, perhaps—and wind up causing an accident because the pilot took so much of his precious time worrying about what eventually is determined to have been no problem at all.

While instrument pilots probably are more likely to suffer from distraction, VFR pilots are not immune. In one case, a Cessna 182RG landed gear-up at a Florida airport. The pilot was so sure he had extended the landing gear, he told investigators that after touching down, he felt a shimmy in the nose of the aircraft before the airplane settled to the runway. A check of the runway surface showed scrape marks where the aircraft slid on its belly. The landing gear displayed no damage of the type investigators expected to find had the gear been extended before landing and retracted after touching down.

What might have distracted the Skylane pilot during his landing approach sufficiently to make him forget to extend the landing gear? We don't know that for sure, but we can speculate, because almost every unintentional gear-up landing is caused by a distraction of one kind or another. Sometimes, a controller asks the pilot to keep his speed up or to make an unusually short approach. The pilot then focuses on the traffic he is following or the runway, itself, and, because his routine has been disturbed, he neglects to extend the landing gear.

In another case, a student pilot on short final at a Louisiana airport was startled when another airplane taxied onto the runway at an intersection about 1,000 feet down and began its takeoff roll. The student, flying a Cessna 152, felt he was too close to go around and elected to land behind the departing aircraft. Upon touchdown, the Cessna bounced hard three times, and the nose wheel collapsed. The airplane then ran off the left side of the runway, damaging the right wing, after the student applied full left rudder, thinking that would keep the Cessna from flipping over onto its back. This student pilot became distracted to the point where he focused too much of his attention on the departing aircraft and neglected to fly *his* airplane.

Self-Discipline

So, how do we keep distractions from ruining our day? The solution is simple enough: It's called self-discipline. But, the nature of flying airplanes and the multitude of things that can happen during flight make its application difficult. For example, a gear-up landing can be prevented by using a checklist of some sort as you enter the traffic pattern. Once *in* the pattern, it's difficult to use a written checklist because you need to be looking for other traffic at the same time; but, a mental checklist will suffice. Some pilots like to have the gear extended before entering the pattern, and that may work, depending on the airplane you are flying and the speed that you need. Others don't like to extend the gear until they are established on the downwind leg. Such habits work well if you fly exactly the same pattern each time. But, every landing is different, and circumstances change, depending on how much traffic you have ahead of you. Also, what if you are landing at a controlled airport and don't enter the downwind leg?

This is where self-discipline enters the picture. You must train yourself to complete the checklist at approximately the same point every time. That point may be outside the traffic pattern, it could be a given distance from touchdown, or it might be at a given altitude, such as pattern altitude. Whatever method you decide upon, you must practice it to the point where it becomes second nature. Like flaring the airplane for touchdown, completing your "before landing" checklist becomes automatic.

Remember, when a pilot becomes distracted, he normally forgets something. His attention is diverted to the point where he is no longer concentrating on flying the airplane, and he bends metal because he fails to do something that should be habitual, like extending the landing gear or maintaining flying speed. A pilot who has trained himself to the point where accomplishing the "before landing" checklist and maintaining flying speed become second nature is much less likely to fall victim to distraction than one who has no concept of accomplishing his cockpit and flying duties routinely. And, as part of that routine, you build in some safeguards.

Good Habits

Years ago, I knew a pilot who would always pull the throttle(s) to idle for a second on final approach to see if the gear horn would go off. This gave him one more indication that the gear was down and locked. This was a backup to his "before landing" checklist and a safeguard against landing with the gear up. The practice apparently worked well for this pilot, because, to my knowledge, he never landed an airplane gear-up.

There are many reasons why I prefer not to pull the throttle(s) of a high-performance airplane to idle on final approach. I am not criticizing that pilot's method, but this is 20 years later, and we know a lot more about engine operation and how to help an engine reach TBO than we did back in those days. There are other ways to verify that the gear are down and locked. My backup is to check for a "gear safe" indication on final approach. I have become so used to checking those lights on final that recently, while flying a Cessna 172, I found myself looking down for the lights on final. Many twins have mirrors positioned on the left engine cowl so the pilot can see that the nose gear is in position. That, along with the green light(s) on the panel, can provide verification.

There are many other examples, but you get the idea. If you establish habit patterns that include double-checking critical elements, although you still might miss one step if your attention is diverted, you should not miss the verification of that step. This holds for many important items, like positioning of the fuel selectors, flaps and fuel pump switches. Most "before takeoff" checklists include critical items twice, and one should never be in a hurry when using the checklist.

Habit patterns involving the setting of in-flight items like nav radios can be practiced with the same double diligence. For instance, sometime after setting up your ILS or VOR approach, but before you intercept the final approach course, you should go back and verify that you have the correct frequencies and OBS settings selected.

For the most part, habit patterns which make aircraft control predominant and ensure double-checking of critical procedures should keep you out of trouble. But, there are times when a pilot perceives a threat so large that he is tempted to focus his complete attention on it.

At such times, caution must be taken to avoid undue distraction, no matter what's going on.

Let's use the example of losing an engine in a twin. That's a drastic situation which definitely deserves *some* of your attention. If it happens during takeoff on a hot, humid day in an airplane that is at or near gross weight, you will have your hands full. That's why the emergency procedure, which emphasizes aircraft control, is repeatedly drilled during multiengine training. However, there are other emergency and abnormal conditions that require analysis and decisions before action is taken. An example is an instrument failure or malfunction that requires a pilot to fly partial panel. The key is to be prepared for the situation. And that means training. The more you practice for that event, the faster you will be able to recognize the problem and react to it while still scanning the important instruments that are going to help you keep the airplane in the air until you are ready to set it down in a field or are sure you can make it around the traffic pattern.

Problem Passengers

Less drastic but potentially deadly distractions are likely to come from passengers or crew members, controllers, other airplanes in your vicinity, misplaced charts or approach plates, secondary systems that are not working properly and a host of items that will tempt you to forget that you are flying an airplane.

I have had several incidents with passengers over the years which seem a bit funny today, though I would not want to relive them. In one case, five passengers managed to board a Cessna 310 without revealing that their visit to the "trough of the hot spirits" was just a bit longer than necessary. As soon as the wheels left the runway, though, calamity broke out in the cabin. Fortunately, the fellow sitting next to me was big and, for the most part, sober. He took my rather loud direction and settled the cabin down enough to encourage me to decide to continue the flight. However, there were some flare-ups to come, and I missed several radio calls because my headset was ripped from my head and there was so much noise that I couldn't hear the speaker. Flying the airplane was not easy, but I paid extra attention to that primary task while keeping an eye on the goings-on in the cabin. My "bouncer" helped immensely. Had he been part of the problem, rather than the solution, I don't know what would have happened.

The incident shows that you can't always anticipate problems from passengers that will distract you from your flying. Of course, you should never allow someone who's obviously intoxicated to board your airplane. If a person appears to be ill, make certain another passenger can attend him or her if something unexpected occurs, so you can continue flying the airplane. But, often, the passengers who cause the worst problems are not ill or intoxicated. They are talkers. They sit next to the pilot so they can share their limited knowledge of aviation and don't shut their mouths from the time the door closes until it opens again. Some don't even wait for an invitation before helping themselves to the radios or the controls! You have to be firm with these people and not allow them to interfere with your duties. I flew a Cessna 421 once with a passenger who began talking incessantly as soon as we climbed up front. He was a pilot, so I asked him if he would like to do the radio work. He readily agreed, but that didn't stop him from chatting. He missed several radio calls that I had to respond to. He apologized each time. Finally, I asked politely if he could tone it down a little so I could concentrate on what I was doing. He stopped talking...for all of three minutes.

Diverted Attention

Pilots sometimes create their own distractions by *purposely* allowing their attention to wander from aircraft control. For example, a pilot buzzing a house in hilly terrain is likely not to notice that when he makes his first pass, he is climbing, following the terrain. He is looking at his audience directly below him, so his true attitude is deceiving. On the second pass, he reduces his airspeed a little more and flies a little lower, wanting those below him to see him wave. Just as he passes over the house, the airplane stalls. The pilot panics and causes the airplane to spin. He is too low to recover.

Another pilot in the right seat may be helpful when something occurs that requires too much of your attention. But, if he has no knowledge of that particular aircraft's systems, you must be cautious when asking him to do something. In fact, it might be better, under some circumstances, to let him fly the airplane straight and level while you troubleshoot the problem to prevent compounding it. In those situations, you must stay ahead of the airplane while working on the offending system. Another pilot who is only going to interfere with problem-solving is of no use to you. Autopilots are a great help when something other than flying the airplane requires your attention. But, remember, they only respond to *your* commands. If you don't pay attention to what the autopilot is doing, you could find yourself in the same predicament as the pilot who became distracted to the point where he lost control of the airplane. Working on a problem while monitoring the autopilot is much easier than trying to fly the airplane and troubleshoot.

The best way to avoid becoming distracted from flying the airplane is training. Recurrency training is just as important as your basic training because it teaches you to keep your awareness levels high. If we were to rate a pilot's "awareness factor" on a scale of one to 10, a high level of awareness would be a 10, while a one would indicate no awareness at all. A pilot who regularly scans the instrument panel, whether flying VFR or IFR, is likely to be at the upper end of the scale. He is looking for anything that might indicate a problem is about to occur. Of course, the earlier he catches it, the less of a distraction it will be. A pilot who is busy talking to a passenger, letting the autopilot fly the airplane, and paying no attention to the instruments or looking out the window, will pay for his laxity when a problem develops, because it will be a total surprise to him. By the time he becomes aware of it, it will require much more of his attention than it would have, had he noticed it earlier. His awareness factor will be much lower than it would have been if he were paying attention and watching for unusual developments.

So, distractions *can* be managed, providing the pilot has a high awareness factor, is current and proficient, and has a good knowledge of the aircraft and its systems. Spotting a potential problem before it develops into a major situation that may take your attention away from your primary duty of flying the airplane will save you much grief. Don't allow passengers to draw your attention from your work, and be aware that even a call from a controller, at the wrong moment, can distract you long enough to keep you from safely completing your flight.

Section Three

The Go/No-Go Decision

A Personal
Question

I n this section we'll examine the most important decision of all: whether or not to take off in the first place. For many instrument pilots, the answer to this question lies in the weather reports, and that's that. But, there's more to it than whether there's a line of thunderstorms in the way or if the destination is below minimums.

But, there's more to it than that. To make the go/no go decision intelligently, an instrument pilot has to consider his or her own fitness, and the health of the airplane as well. We'll go into detail on these topics in the next few chapters. First, though, is the outline of a simple and effective risk assessment system from ex-Naval aviator and current King Air pilor David Mitchell.

Is This Flight Too Risky?

Risk management is a subject that every pilot is familiar with, yet most of us can't explain what it really means in simple language. And even if you could explain it on Monday, your explanation might be different by Friday, since risk tolerance tends to be a moving target.

A go/no-go decision is based on the willingness to accept a certain level of risk. The FARs, company policy and rules of thumb provide guidance, but ultimately, there's no fail-safe way to make the call. Sometimes, disagreements over what's safe and what's not get so heated that job terminations result.

A classic example occurred several years ago when a Memphis-based Beech 1900 pilot refused to fly a trip with an inop air conditioning/pressurization system. Apparently the company's ops specs and MEL allowed the flight when flown at 10,000 feet or below. But the pilot refused on the grounds that since it was the middle of the summer, older passengers would be subjected to undue heat stress and turbulence.

When he was fired, he took his case to the local newspaper, but so did the airline. Accusations were traded back and forth over several weeks.

The pilot won the initial skirmish, but ultimately lost the war since he probably won't work for another airline.

Most pilots can identify with his plight and might concur that it was a point worth making a career decision over. The question is, in similar circumstances, could you logically explain your reasoning or would you just say "it doesn't feel right?"

A Basic Formula

During my to years as a Navy pilot, which included assignments as a safety officer. I encountered quite a few risk evaluation techniques. Unfortunately, most were neither simple nor memorable. Anything that requires a pencil, paper and a calculator may not be used on a daily basis. That doesn't mean these systems have no value: just that many of us prefer something simpler. One method you've probably heard of is called the "life change" system, whereby points are added up for stressful life situations (we'll talk more about this in the next chapter). Any score above a certain value, says the theory, indicates that the pilot is liable to be too distracted to fly a safe trip. This method fails on several counts, not the least of which is that it focuses solely on the person, without much regard to other variables, including weather and the airplane.

The method I'll explain here is a conglomeration of all the systems I've seen over the years, but is much simpler. Its basis is a ready-room lecture by a wise old squadron safety officer.

He introduced the idea of evaluating risk using only three categories: the Man, the Machine, and the Environment. I started using this method to explain to students how to sense when they were about to get in over their heads.

The categories of man, machine and environment provide a convenient mnemonic that's practically self-explanatory. The technique is to evaluate each category and isolate any negative influences which could impact the flight. The degree of detail is up to you. If you think something could affect the flight, include it in your analysis; just don't get carried away. Scratches on the windshield or forgetting to get your flu shot are probably not significant. But a failed autopilot during single-pilot IFR or a head cold definitely are. Keep a simple scorecard in your head as you tally up the negatives.

Personally, my rule of thumb for evaluating the risk is simply this:

A total of one or two negatives in separate categories won't make me say no but will require more-than-normal vigilance.

At three total, with one in each category, I'll be looking for solid-gold options in all categories if the worst case should occur. If two occur within a category, I'11 devote special attention to my options.

At a total of four negative, things are getting complicated. One category has at least two and all categories have something I don't like. Three items in one category might be grounds for cancellation.

At five, "pucker factor" is definitely coming into play. A three-two or four-one combination will probably leave few options in the affected categories and thus be cause for cancellation.

At six, regardless of the distribution, cancellation should be considered. The risk factors are getting too complex unless you still have realistic options available in each category if the worst happens. Add another negative, for a total of seven, and it's time to call it a day, no matter what.

Nit-Picks and Oversights

The key to making this system work is striking the right balance between nit-picking every detail and disregarding serious discrepancies. My rule is that a factor counts if it causes me to do something different from my normal routine or if it rules out an option. Of course, any single factor that involves a violation of a FAR, company policy, POH guidance or just plain common sense, is grounds for cancellation.

Try not to get hung up on which category to assign something. A negative is a negative. For example, where would you put a problem passenger, man or environment? The time to worry about this is if there are already two factors in a category and your next item makes a third. If you must, split it between categories. The point is not the negative factors, but the options that are left when the worst happens. A large, complex aircraft probably has enough system redundancy and the crew is trained well enough so that a safe flight could be made with failures that would ground a small aircraft. The same goes for the crew. A well-trained airline or military crew that has recently been through a thorough simulator refresher can stand more problems than a rusty single-pilot who's barely proficient on the gauges.

Some Examples

Let's look at a hypothetical example.

Start with a fully equipped aircraft crewed by a well-rested, trained pilot and copilot on a VMC day, the kind of trip where you hear pilots say "and they pay me to do this." It's obviously a zero-point situation.

The chief danger is that complacency might cause a fatal oversight.

Now throw in IMC, an autopilot that randomly drops altitude hold and a copilot who was just handed divorce papers. You now need to devote attention in all three categories. These three factors could combine into an accident scenario and yet with reasonable diligence, most pilots would agree that the circumstances don't warrant a cancellation.

Let's continue the what-if game. Suppose the destination is in mountainous terrain with weather near minimums, some of the cockpit lights have failed and the pilot and copilot don't communicate well. One strike in each category, two of which (man and environment) may not be fixable.

Throw in another unexpected mechanical or unforecast icing and you could easily go over the top right into an accident.

Let's look at two real world examples. You may have read about a recent accident involving an FAA Flight Check King Air that flew into a mountain in Virginia after departing into marginal VFR without an IFR clearance. The mission was a day and-half behind schedule and the crew was trying to get to the next destination before their duty day expired. The NTSB's investigation revealed a number of troubling incidents in the PIC's background that his supervisors had ignored. He had two DUIs and his driving license was currently under suspension at the time of the accident. He had recently received a letter of reprimand for damaging an engine during start.

The vast majority of copilots in his office avoided flying with him. Several had confronted him and his supervisors about his poor judgment, but no management action was taken, for which the NTSB faulted the FAA.

Applying the risk assessment system, three to five negative factors are obvious in the man column alone.

Throwing in the marginal VFR and the schedule pressure, two more points appear. No aircraft deficiencies are mentioned and were apparently not factors. This flight was definitely in the extreme caution range and might have been well into the cancellation category.

Another example had a happier ending. A Boeing 767 departed Chicago for Frankfurt, Germany, Weather at Frankfurt was forecast to be 200-foot ceiling and 300 meters visibility, but this aircraft and crew were Cat IIIB qualified down to a 15-foot DH and 125 meters RVR. Weather was thus not a serious factor. The aircraft had no maintenance gripes. Fuel calculations indicated there would be a generous margin at the destination.

During the climbout, a tiny pressurization leak occurred in the copilot's sliding window, producing an uncomfortably loud whistle but no real hazard. After discussing the situation with company maintenance, the crew decided to remain at FL 270 (lower than normal) and tuck wet paper towels into the gap. This fixed the noise, but at the cost of considerably higher fuel consumption. New calculations showed that the destination fuel would only be 200 pounds above reserve, plus alternate fuel requirements. There was no margin for error or additional unexpected developments. The crew discussed the options. At the coast-out-point, all aircraft systems were functioning, the weather was acceptable at the destination and at alternate and en route alternates, which are required for two-engine overwater operations. The crew agreed that if any other complications arose, a fuel stop would be made.

Hours later, as the flight approached Ireland, the weather was improving slightly at Frankfurt. A closer but equally acceptable alternate was chosen, yielding an additional 1500 pounds of contingency fuel. While still in British airspace, the crew declared minimum fuel so that ATC in Frankfurt wouldn't be surprised. The flight was handled expeditiously and landed within 200 pounds of the coast-out-point estimate.

The crew had, in effect, been using the risk management system I've described here. They analyzed all the negative factors and options, then set conservative go/no-go criteria. Assigning values to their decisionmaking, my analysis gives one point for the weather and one point for the mechanical problem for two points total. The crew set the no-go criteria at three points total, probably because there aren't many options when you don't have enough fuel.

Add It All Up

In summary, look at the three categories and keep a running total. At the same time, identify your options and outs if things go bad. If you have no outs left in a category or the number of factors totals six or more, it's time to cancel the flight. If you're a fly-for-hire type and your boss views the situation differently, you can provide a concise explanation for your reasoning. And if it comes to it, you'll be prepared to make that career decision.

Pilot
Fitness

*I*f you're incapable of making proper, clear and *rational decisions when called upon to do so, you're an unsafe pilot. It's as simple as that.*

Part of that process has to do with your attitude, but even the best of us can be rendered unsafe if enough external stresses are brought to bear.

An instrument pilot must perform flawlessly under pressure. It's vital that the pilot be up to the task of completing the flight successfully. So the first part of the go/no-go question should be: "How do I feel today?"

Jack King, a former test and corporate pilot with 20,000 hours, here offers some words on keeping within your own personal performance envelope.

Stretching the Human Envelope

We all recognize that exceeding the established limitations of any aircraft's operating envelope has the potential of resulting in a catastrophe. However, there is another envelope that is equally as important to aviation safety. During routine flight operations, there is a normal tendency to overlook the safety factors involved in exceeding the operating limits of the human envelope.

Several factors relating to an aircraft's operating envelope are similar to those of the human envelope. In the man/machine relationship, the typical aircraft usually can greatly surpass most endurance as well as performance characteristics of the human element. Aircraft are designed and constructed to operate at rather high limits of stress and pressure. By comparison, the human element must either adapt or fail to function properly. This type of failure may be referred to as exceeding the limits of the human envelope. In the interest of safety, these associated factors should be recognized in order to either avoid or cope with the associated adverse conditions. Several examples of exceeding these limits will be discussed in this chapter.

Unlike scheduled airline and charter pilots, most private and corporate pilots are not governed by specific flight duty limitations and mandatory rest periods. Obviously, the freedom from such limitations in Part 91 is often misused, and this has been a significant factor leading to many minor incidents as well as serious accidents. Let's take a look at a few examples relating to overextending the human envelope. Perhaps, the most common occurrence relates to our natural urge to get home--and to take unnecessary risks, knowingly or unwittingly, to do so.

The natural desire to complete a return flight home is often referred to as "get-home-itis." This often self-induced pressure can result in exceeding the limitations of the typical private pilot, especially when adverse weather conditions exist. Unfortunately, in addition to the limitations of the aircraft, many pilots do not fully recognize their own limitations relating to flight proficiency and may completely overlook their own human envelope factors, such as physical well-being and proper rest.

Dozing Off

There are many routine situations which may seem insignificant but, when compounded by inadequate pilot judgment, may be cited as the probable cause of an avoidable incident or accident. For example: Falling asleep on a night approach and landing in brushy terrain short of the runway seems highly unlikely, but quite a few years ago, this actually happened to a fellow pilot.

My friend, a senior pilot who's still flying, told me of his experience, which, I believe, most of us can relate to: After completing an unusually long daylight flight and dropping off his passenger, he decided to take advantage of the good weather and make the long return trip, even though it meant flying most of the night without rest.

After many uneventful hours in the light twin, he was making a late-night fuel stop when he inadvertently "dozed off" for a few moments while descending on the approach. The weird sound of scraping brush abruptly awakened him; but, at that point, it was too late to recover. Fortunately, he was not seriously hurt. Today, he will enthusiastically caution fellow pilots not to exceed the human envelope by attempting excessively long flights without sufficient rest and sleep.

Although there are absolutely no limits on flight time or minimum rest requirements when flying as a private or corporate pilot under Part

91 of the FARs, it should be of interest to learn what has been considered the safe limits established for scheduled and charter pilots.

Under current regulations, pilots flying scheduled operations under Part 135 are limited to 34 hours per week, 120 hours per month and 1,200 hours per year, whereas pilots flying domestic operations under Part 121 are limited to 30 hours per week, 100 hours per month and 1,000 hours per year. Regulations governing minimum rest for pilots are the same for Part 135 and Part 121 operators. Basically, for a scheduled flight time of from eight to nine hours, the minimum rest period in the 24 hours before duty is from nine to 11 hours. The required rest period may be slightly reduced if the rest period following duty is increased.

Even though a Part 91 pilot is not subject to any limitations on flight and duty time, or required to abide by specified rest periods, it is highly advisable when planning extensive flight operations to keep in mind the regulations governing airline and charter pilots and to establish conservative limits for your primary objective of recognizing that stretching the human envelope can greatly increase the risks of flying.

(Although the limitations on flight and duty time, and the rest requirements specified in Parts 135 and 121 can be used as guidelines, they certainly are no guarantee that the human envelope won't be stretched. Indeed, about nine out of every 10 pilots interviewed by NTSB for a recent commuter airline safety study pointed out scheduling factors that caused them to fly while fatigued, despite the regulations. That's why we stress adoption of conservative personal limits.)

Stress is another factor which can easily stretch the human envelope to the breaking point. We all experience stress to varying degrees. Some of us are able to cope with stress better than others, but we all have limits that, when exceeded, can adversely affect our ability to perform in the cockpit. An overload of stress can cause pilots to make mistakes, forget standard procedures and even lose normal judgment--a situation we referred to during World War II flight training as having your "head up and locked."

Medical experts have compiled a rather interesting table of factors which can help predict the physical problems that can result from too much change and stress in a person's life. This table (the "Holmes/Rahe Life Change Scale") assigns a point value to some 43 items which can result in life changes relating to stress. The table has provided the basis for development of several stress-scoring tools for flight crew members. For example, the table which accompanies this article was developed, in part, from surveys of airline pilots. To determine your individual level of stress, you can refer to the chart for tabulation of the point values for any of the various situations which you may have recently experi-

Pilot Stress Test

Are You Fit to Fly?

This test was developed, in part, from surveys of 1,032 airline pilots by the Aviation Research and Education Foundation. Though a few of the questions apply specifically to airline pilots, they could, with some thought, be tailored to parallel the circumstances appropriate to those who fly for business, pleasure or personal transportation. The evaluation cannot be considered a precise quantitative assessment of stress because the effects of stress on individuals are so diverse. However, the foundation suggests that a score of 75 or more should indicate that there may be reason to consider attempting to reduce stress before an upcoming flight.

1. Have you had a death in the immediate family? **50**

2. Has someone in your immediate family experienced a serious health problem recently? **37**

3. Are you feeling uncertain about your mate, and is there the possibility of an extramarital affair? **36**

4. Have you had a serious disagreement with, or do you fly with an incompatible crew member? **35**

5. Have you had insufficient rest between flights or recently completed a "red-eye" flight? **34**

6. Are you having serious difficulties with your children? **33**

7. Do you have a fundamental disagreement with the management style of your airline? **32**

8. Do you suspect alcohol or drug use by crew members? **32**

9. Are you experiencing an unstable or uneasy home life? **32**

10. Have you recently had a serious disagreement with your mate? **31**

enced, then total the point values. In theory, the point value total can predict the extent to which you are at risk of having stress significantly affect your performance in the cockpit.

Such a self-analysis might confirm the extent of your stress by reviewing and confirming the problems which are causing you the most worry. For example, if matters or problems of health, finances, security, marriage, working conditions, etc., are of serious concern, you should make an attempt to resolve these matters outside the cockpit. Our public libraries are filled with books on stress-management and related subjects. There is an old adage about learning to accept what you can't change; and, even in our dog-eat-dog society, many problems often can be eliminated by a fresh outlook or a new approach.

Stretching the human envelope with excessive pressure or stressful situations usually can be relieved when the cause is removed, but I recall one case in which the resulting situation apparently could not be reversed. This incident involved a good friend and fellow corporate pilot several years ago, when he was flying a Gulfstream I for a major corporation. Through an unexpected move, he was promoted to chief pilot, and he decided that since the company was also operating two other business jet models, he should obtain type ratings for the other airplanes as soon as possible. He proceeded to FlightSafety and, on a greatly accelerated training program including both day and night sessions, soon completed the necessary training and obtained his type rating for the company's Jetstar. Then,

without taking a break, he proceeded with his hectic schedule to pursue a type rating for the company's Hawker in as little time as possible. Apparently, the pressure was too great: While flying the simulator, he developed a severe case of vertigo which eventually resulted in the loss of his medical certificate. My friend was forced to take an early retirement from the flight department.

This example shows what excessive, self-induced pressure can do. It should serve to remind us to avoid being trapped in any type of overly hectic scheduling that has the possibility of developing into a similar treadmill type of situation. Another well-worn bit of advice seems appropriate here: Make sure you take time to stop and smell the roses.

Killer Schedules

To further illustrate the adverse results of stretching the human envelope with a hectic schedule, I would like to relate the story of a corporate pilot with whom I came in contact as the part-time managing editor of Professional Pilot Magazine back in 1968. This pilot flew a de Havilland Dove for a major typewriter manufacturer, and he proposed an article written in the style of an elementary-school primer. Here are portions of his article, "Run, Jim, Run," which appeared under the pseudonym "Roger Straightenlevel":

"See Jim run. Jim is a pilot. He is running to get ready to take off with the Big Man at eight o'clock. See the clock. The big hand is straight up. The little hand is straight out at the left side. Jim is still running. He is now running to the telephone. The Big Man tells Jim they will take off at 10 o'clock.... The weather is getting worse. The rain is now making ice on the airplane. Jim runs to find a man to take the ice off the airplane. The Big Man will be here soon and will want to fly away. Jim cannot find the ice man. He tears his gloves and trousers and hands getting the ice off the airplane. Jim runs to the bathroom. Jim runs to the telephone to tell Radio he will not be ready to go at 10 o'clock, as the Big Man is not here yet.

"The Big Man gives Jim a letter. The letter tells Jim to fly to Atlanta and get Mr. Jones. Mr. Jones tells Jim to hurry to Boston. They do. Jim runs to the telephone at Boston. The Big Man is ready to come home. It is dark. It is cold. It is still raining. Jim is running slowly now. He flies to Phoenix to get the Big Man. Big Man is not at the airport. He is having a late dinner and a soft drink with olives in it. See the clock now. The big hand is straight up. The little hand is straight up again. The Big Man likes olives. Jim runs very slowly to meet Big Man. Jim flies Big Man home. See the clock now. Jim is not running. He will run again at daylight. He will run up to Boston to get Mr. Jones...."

It was unfortunate that this interesting account could not have been the start of a more rewarding literary venture; but, a short time later, the Dove crashed into Lake Michigan, killing the pilot, the CEO and his family.

As a former corporate pilot, I can relate to this pilot's busy schedule. Following World War II, there was a surplus of qualified military pilots and just having a flying job was regarded as a prize. The concept of corporate aviation was new, and most pilots were gung-ho to work long hours just to prove the value of air transportation to business. During this era, I flew a converted DC-3, and we seldom canceled a trip unless the airlines also were grounded.

In later years, after the National Business Aircraft Association was organized, many flight departments added standards for scheduling and crew rest periods to their operating manuals. Unfortunately, excessive scheduling apparently still is a problem in a few flight departments. In one case, a good friend chose to take early retirement after his company frowned upon flight crews stopping for rest during international flights.

Improving With Age

My friend Dick Henson, at age 84, admits he "might be stretching the human envelope slightly" by obtaining a type rating in the new Learjet 31 he recently purchased for personal transportation. But, Henson, who is still chairman of the board of USAir Express, a major commuter airline he developed, is very vocal on the importance of maintaining a healthy lifestyle.

During a recent interview, he passed along some tips he learned from his own experience: Diet and exercise are the priorities he emphasizes. He recommends fish and chicken, and either jogging or some other form of regular exercise. In addition to the Learjet, Henson also operates a 45-foot motorhome, which he drove some 6,500 miles last summer. "This also helps keep me sharp," he commented. For "relaxation," he still flies his Pitts biplane.

Another excellent example of a pilot who made an effort to remain physically and mentally sharp is the late Capt. Dick Merrill, who at age 78 hand-flew a Lockheed L-1011 on a record-breaking delivery flight from Palmdale, Calif. to Miami at 710 mph. Merrill also placed great emphasis on a healthy lifestyle. He did not smoke or drink, was very select with his diet and enjoyed jogging on a regular basis.

Also, there's my fishing buddy Bill Morris, who at age 88 owns a well-equipped Cessna 182 which we flew from Maryland to the AOPA convention in California last fall. To avoid stretching our envelopes, we traded legs and made four overnight stops during the enjoyable, 36-hour flight.

As these senior airmen have proved, age, alone, does not have to be a factor in stretching the human envelope. A proper respect for good health habits, combined with special emphasis on a reasonable diet, exercise and proper rest, will not only result in enhancing the quality of life, but will result in an extension of the normally accepted age milestones. Obviously, adopting this lifestyle pattern at a much younger age can be very rewarding in later years.

Rest and Recreation

Perhaps, most of us are guilty of not balancing our day-to-day work schedules with proper recreation. The old adage, "All work and no play makes Jack a dull boy," can be expanded to conclude that all work and insufficient rest can rupture the human envelope and certainly jeopardize flight safety.

Obviously, the most healthful form of recreation also involves some type of physical exercise, since this is a very important factor in our general well-being, as well as for clearing any cobwebs of stress from our minds. Proper exercise can be attained from various activities, such as jogging, swimming, bicycling, tennis, golf, etc. When these activities are not convenient, the experts recommend plenty of walking. Thus, when time is not a factor, even bypassing the FBO's courtesy car and walking on the ramp will provide some beneficial exercise.

In light of all the above, it could be instructive the next time you review an aircraft accident report to comprehend the actions of the pilot involved and try to determine if stretching the human envelope may have been an unreported factor. Such human factors are usually thoroughly explored by NTSB in airline accidents but are not investigated deeply in GA accidents.

I hope the examples provided in this article will serve as a reminder of the importance of monitoring your own lifestyle as well as your flight scheduling, so that work pressure and stress will not stretch the limits of your human envelope.

(And, in the interest of safety, don't hesitate to offer advice to a fellow pilot if you believe he or she is operating at the edge of their envelope.)

For your efforts in complying with these operational challenges, the rewards will not only include greater enjoyment of your flying experience, but, also, as a bonus, will reflect in a much higher standard of safety, as well as greatly enhanced longevity.

Checking
the Airplane

Familiarity breeds contempt. While most pilots are careful about preflights, it's easy to fall into the trap of looking at something without really seeing it. Ever see a pilot look in the oil door, take a cursory glance, and then continue with the preflight without actually examining the airplane's powerplant? It happens all the time.

It's especially important to be dilligent on your preflight when you're about to launch into IMC. What might be an inconvenience on a VFR flight can be fatal on an instrument departure.

Are You Sure It Will Fly?

We spend a lot of time preparing for and IFR flight. When we go out to fly in the soup we should feel good about our abilities. But what about the airplane we're going to fly?

FAR 91.7 states: "The pilot in command of a civil aircraft is responsible for determining whether that aircraft is in condition for safe flight."

There are many ways to look at that statement. Most of us aren't mechanics, so, are we responsible for hte internal workings of the engine and other parts when we lack control over their operational condition? In one sense, we are.

The regulations require us to determine that the airplane is maintained within the regulations that apply, and there are no outstanding discrepancies that would make the machine unairworthy. For example, if your airplane has just come out of annual inspection, and your mechanic has signed the log books (indicating that the airplane is airworthy), is that enough for you to jump in and go? No, it isn't. What if the mechanic didn't tighted all the cowl screws or forgot to add oil to the engine? Whose fault is that?

Now, transpose either of these problems to a low-IFR departure and where does that leave you? Probably sitting in a field somewhere, scratching your head (if you're lucky).

So, you're responsible for the condition of the aircraft when you depart, and that's why a good preflight inspection is necessary. the preflight should start before you get to the airport.

Can You Check Status?

For example, if you belong to a flying club, how do you know the airplane is airworthy when so many other people fly it? If the airplane is hangared, and everyone has a key, is there an easily accessible record that indicates when the inspections are due, and lists any deficiencies that other pilots have reported? If you just get in the airplane and fly without knowing its real status, you could be setting yourself up for a fall.

We saw a student pilot and his flight instructor fly a Cessna 150 to an airport for a private pilot checkride when the airplane was out of annual. They didn't check the logbooks before they left home. (That one resulted in an entire wasted day for the student, instructor, and examiner while they scared up another airplane. Fortunately, the student passed.)

In another incident, a renter-pilot attempted to start a Cessna 172, only to have a fire erupt in the engine compartment. Mechanics had removed carburetor parts for repair, and only a handful of cowl screws were holding it in place. However, there was nothing in the cockpit to warn the pilot.

The first post-annual flight in a large twin was fatal for the two pilots on board some years back. The ailerons had been rigged backwards, and they didn't bother with a control check.

Incidents like these occur when pilots don't pay enough attention to the airplanes they fly. It's one thing when you're the sole owner/ operator, but it's another entirely when there are others involved.

Instrument flying is tough enough without having to resolve mechanical problems while airborne. Many pilots don't fly instruments often enough to deal with major problems as easily and confidently as they should. When you're in the clouds, any problem that occurs can be major.

Preflight the Logs

Start your preflight by reviewing the log books and/or other records your club or organization uses to indicate the status of each airplane. Log books are hte best, but some organizations don't have these records readily available for customers to peruse. The records are often locked in a filing cabinet, accessible only to the person responsible for maintenance. It's normal, however, to have a status sheet, bulletin board, chalk board, or the like to indicate the exact status of each airplane a club or operator has on its line.

This information should indicate the inspection status of the airplane and any other maintenance that will be due in the future. Then, it's a simple matter to compare the hobbs or tach time of the aircraft with the information provided. Some maintenance items are accomplished by date and should be listed that way.

The next step is a thorough preflight inspection. Again, if you're the only pilot who flies the airplane, the preflight is just as important, but at least you're familiar with its mechanical condition from the previous flight. If you fly a club or rental aircraft, you don't know what the last pilot experienced. It pays to look a lot closer in case something occurred that wasn't reported.

If you're going to depart into IFR conditions that won't allow you to return VFR, be alert for problems that would be a minimal distraction on a VFR day, but can be severe on an IFR day.

For example, a blocked pitot tube or static port could cause all kinds of problems. Faulty airspeed, VSI, or altimeter readings just after breaking ground have caused fatal accidents in IFR conditions. An open door, if not dealt with correctly, is worse on a day when you don't want to take your eyes off the instruments during takeoff. If you can return visually to the airport to close the door, it's much less nerve-wracking on you and your passengers than having to shoot an instrument approach just to fix it. It's unlikely you'll be able to close the door while airborne anyhow, so if it does pop open, don't lose control in the clouds by diverting your attention to it.

Walk-Around Checks

These are just a couple of items that should be dealt with before committing to flight. A good walk-around should reveal items such as trim tabs that are left at full deflection. This is likely to occur in a twin following a training flight, where single-engine operations were practiced, or in an airplane just out of maintenance. Any cables or wiring that can be reached should be inspected. We've found alternator cables that would have broken during a flight. Exhaust systems should be inspected for security as much as is possible.

Fuel tanks must be visually checked before any flight, but it's even more important for an instrument trip. If you're expecting full tanks, and depending on maximum fuel for flight planning, make sure it's there. A silent engine in the clouds is much more difficult to deal with than one that occurs in VFR conditions.

Some accessories aren't necessary for VFR flight, but are vital for instrument conditions. Check all the lights visually, not just by a drop on the ammeter (yes, this does mean a couple of trips into the cockpit to flip switches). Make certain the pitot heat is actually functioning, and that nothing's blocked the tube. Deice equipment should be checked for function, and any consumables (alcohol, glycol) topped up.

Insist that your club or rental operation place "grounding" flags on the yoke when an aircraft is known to be unairworthy.This helps prevent anyone from operating the airplane who didn't know there was a problem with it. In fact, the first thing you should do when beginning your actual preflight is look inside the cockpit for a flag or note from the previous pilot.

After completing a walk-around, and once you're satisfied the aircraft is airworthy, you aren't out of the woods yet. There are several more items to check. These are actually part of the preflight, but normally occur after engine start.

After Engine Start

For example, vacuum is extremely important, especially in a single-engine airplane. Some gauges are placed on the far-right side of the instrument panel. Don't skip looking at the vacuum gauge. Check it immediately after engine start at ground-idle, then again during the runup. A weak vacuum pump can be spotted if it isn't putting out much suction at idle or low rpm, where it would normally be close to its operating range. If you suspect the pump pressure is low, have it checked before you depart. If it quits while you're in the clouds, your partial panel skills will be tested, and hopefully you'll be up to it. The idea is to spot problems before they turn into nightmares.

Also check the other instruments as you taxi for the proper indications. An electric instrument, such as the turn coordinator, normally has a flag or other indicator if it does not receive power. Additionally, when you turn on the master switch at the beginning of your preflight, you should hear an electric turn coordinator gyro start turning. If there's an excess amount of noise coming from the instrument, have it checked. It probably needs to be replaced or overhauled.

Vacuum instruments, such as the attitude and heading indicators, normally need at least five minutes after engine start to spool up to operational speed. During taxi, the attitude indicator should display no more than a five-degree tilt during normal turns once it stabilizes. The heading indicator should agree with the magnetic compass and both should match known runway or taxiway headings. The ball in the turn coordinator should move to the outside of any turns while taxiing, and the turn coordinator itself should correctly indicate that the airplane is turning.

If you're departing into a 1,000 foot ceiling, and you find that something isn't working and you want to return to the ground, fly the traffic pattern and land. However, if the weather is less than VFR, you'll need to complete an instrument approach to return. Depending on the type of problem you encounter, and the airport you're departing, a return might not be possible. This is another reason to conduct a thorough preflight before launching on any IFR flight.

Careful Runup

Your runup should be conducted with equal vigilance. Of course, it doesn't matter whether you're IFR or VFR. The engine must be functioning normally before any departure. An engine that fails just after getting airborne at many airports could lead to an off-airport forced landing, so don't take any chances in that regard.

Recently, we were doing a runup in a Piper Arrow and one mag ran very rough. Leaning the mixture did not fix it, so we went in search of a mechanic. Unfortunately, there was no one around who could help. We removed the top cowl, looked carefully at the spark plug leads and grounding leads to the mags, didn't see anything that looked like a problem, and ran the engine again.

Initially, we thought this was a mag problem, since leaning the engine didn't seem to make a difference. When we ran it a second time, it didn't run as rough, then it cleared up completely. We did a full power runup on the runway before releasing the brakes and took off into VFR skies. The engine ran fine and the problem didn't reappear.

It was apparently a fouled spark plug. That's the first time we've seen that happen in this airplane; unusual, because we fly it a lot. However, there's a perfectly good explanation for it. One of the other owners is working on a commercial ticket, and had been doing multiple takeoffs and landings, simulated engine failures, and other maneuvers that require variable power settings at full-rich mixture. Fouled plugs under these conditions are normal.

There's no question that, had the problem not cleared, our flying for the day would have been scrubbed. That would have been an indication of a bad magneto rather than a fouled plug. And a takeoff, especially into IFR conditions, with an engine that isn't running at 100 percent would be foolish.

One way to look at that incident, or any other like it, is as a warning; a red flag. While it turned out there was nothing wrong with the engne, there could have been. An investigation was warranted. Treat any such indication, whether it's a sluggish flight instrument, a vacuum pump that looks weak, or one of a host of otehr items you look at before taking off with suspicion if it doesn't appear to be performing normally. For many of them it won't matter if the weather is VFR or IFR, and for others you probably could go VFR knowing that you might have a failure along the way. Never depart any airport for any reason if you see an indicationof failure that could jeopardize the aircraft and those who are aboard.

Infrequent Flyers

Now, there's something to be said here about an aircraft that doesn't fly very often. Everything we've mentioned so far applies, but here are other areas that should be carefully reviewed as well. For example, extra fuel should be drained from the sumps to ensure water isn't lurking in places where it might cause an engine failure, especially if the aircraft sat with partially full tanks.

A reasonable search for bird's nests should be made in the spring and summer, especially in the engine compartment, rear fuselage, and wing areas near control cables and control surfaces. While changing a landing light on a Cessna 172 we once owned, we discovered a large bird's nest in the wing that had been there for at least three years (all the time we owned the airplane). It wasn't visible from any other point on the wing, and it didn't interfere with the controls at all. Another airplane we were involved with, a Mooney, had a cavity in the tailcone that made a perfect birdhouse. We'd find at least one or two a year in there.

This problem also occurs on airplanes that are flown regularly. The nests appear so quickly that you'd think some birds must have prefabricated nests.

Commit to Grounding

A final word for pilots who aren't constrained by minimum equipment lists: Make one, and stick to it. It is, of course, ridiculous to cancel a trip if the cigarette lighter isn't working, but what about, say, one of the three strobes? Or one of the boots if it's high summer and there's no ice up there? Or a balky electric trim servo? When it comes to equipment, you should have a zero fault tolerance. If it is not working correctly, fix it, and don't fly in IMC until it's right.

Pay close attention to the bird you're about to fly, especially before departing into IMC. Many things can go wrong, but we know what most of those are. By following reasonable preflight precautions, we can ensure continued safe flying.

What About the Weather?

T he last part of our Man-Machine-Environment equation is the environment. We covered this in detail in an earlier volume of the library (Weather for the IFR Pilot, and in particular the section entitled "What Makes You Say No?"), but we'll revisit the question here with some words on how to get a briefing that will help you answer the go/no-go question properly.

Making that decision is based largely, but not exclusively, on the facts and figures contained in a briefing. The briefer can communicate a lot of information in a more subtle way, and can help a pilot make a good choice when the forecasts aren't quite so cut-and-dried. The ultimate decision rests with the pilot, of course, but the briefer can (and will) do as much as possible to help.

Here we have controller Paul Berge with some guidelines on how to extract that vital go/no-go information from a weather briefing.

Getting a Decent Briefing

Years ago, I was flying a homebuilt across the Mojave Desert (not recommended) and was, frankly, a little lost. After landing at what looked like an abandoned military airfield, I walked into an air conditioned shed which turned out to be a Flight Service Station.

Behind the counter was a briefer named Ed. I asked Ed for a weather briefing from there to Phoenix. Instead of reading from the many charts on the wall, Ed took my arm and escorted me outside. Thinking I'd interrupted his lunch, I was surprised when he explained all about the mountains and desert winds; where to find the Santa Anas and how to avoid turbulence in the mountain passes. It was more a BFR then a briefing. I thanked him, departed and, again, became hopelessly lost. But I knew I'd had a great briefing.

You can still get a face-to-face briefing at today's AFSSs, but chances are, most of the Eds are gone. True, a flight service briefer may seem a redundant go-between if you're used to DUAT, but calling 1-800-WXBRIEF, anywhere in the USA, can get you access to both data and, possibly, respectable interpretation. All you need to do is ask the right questions and avoid the dumb mistakes.

Know What to Ask

While visiting the Fort Dodge AFSS recently, I plugged in with a "controller" named Terry. Even though they never separate air traffic, briefers are now officially air traffic controllers with all the same pay and benefits as the folks who actually pry air traffic apart. This doesn't always set well with the tower and en route bunch but politics aside, Terry was working a briefing position taking phone calls from pilots.

Business was slow, so we had time to talk between calls. Terry happens to be a flight instructor and had a good understanding of both sides of the system. Getting a good briefing isn't always a matter of the luck of the draw. While not every briefer has an ATP, they all have access to the same information. It's up to you, the pilot, to glean the most from them.

As we've said before, nothing frustrates a controller more than dragging information from a pilot. The same applies to flight service specialists. They may expect you to request certain services when you call but they still need to know what you want. If you follow accepted format, you'll tap into a wealth of information given by, for the most part, extremely willing personnel.

Tell the briefer you're planning an IFR flight. This saves him from saying, "VFR flight not recommended." Give your callsign. Don't know which plane you're taking? Make one up. Give the aircraft type. The briefer should have a general awareness of aircraft capability and range when discussing alternatives. Give your departure point and your proposed route of flight.

Your destination is important, "...landing Lancaster." What altitude do you plan? Give a block altitude if you're not sure yet, "...between five and nine thousand." The briefer also wants to know when you plan to leave and how long you'll be en route. Again, give estimates, "...departing in one hour and we should be three hours en route." This provides the briefer a broad picture of your plan and he or she will already be bringing up the weather maps on the screen.

At this point, you can really impress the briefer by telling which type of briefing you'd like: Outlook, Standard or Abbreviated. If you don't specify, the briefer will launch into a standard briefing covering all bases. You may get more information than you want.

The Outlook Briefing

It's the night before the flight, and Channel 8 Action News says foul weather's on the way. Your 6 a.m. departure is looking dubious and you need more information than, "...partly cloudy with thunderboomers by morning." Call AFSS; give the above litany and say, "I'd like an outlook briefing, please." Instantly, the briefer knows to skip the notams and other minutiae. The briefer has access to forecasts stretching as far as 48 hours into the future and covering any portion of the country. If you want the latest forecasts, remember to call at least five minutes after the forecasts come out. New forecasts are issued at 1200Z and 0000Z.

The outlook briefing is for long term planning only. When you actually sit down to plan your trip in the morning, you'll need to call for the standard briefing. With a general picture in mind from the outlook briefing, you will listen to the briefer paint a more timely picture of the weather along your route and any changes from the night before will stand out. The briefing is given in a specific order as spelled out in the FAA manual 7110.10. The more familiar you are with the format, the easier it is to "see" the weather being described.

The first item is always adverse conditions—sigments, convective sigmets, airmets and Center Weather Advisories or CWAs. The synopsis follows, then specifics of current conditions, forecasts and so forth. Most of this stuff is straightforward so I won't bore you with the details. But if there's one point that can bite, it's notams. Every FAA written exam has a question about L, D and FDC notams. Once the written is passed, however, the issue tends to get a little cloudy in everyday use.

The important thing to remember is that FSS will give you all D (distant) and FDC (Flight Data Center) notams for both your departure and destination airports. FDC notams, however, will only be given if not yet published in the biweekly booklet. En route there may pages of notams pertaining to every taxiway, radio tower and NDB over which you may fly. The briefer has to scroll through this mess picking out what he or she considers pertinent to your flight, particularly navaid outages.

The briefer will give you the L notams (local) for your departure airport—assuming it's within that AFSS's area—but *not* the L notams for your destination, unless the flight is concluded inside their area. In other words, you may be told about the 75-foot crane operating off the end of runway 32L at your departure airport, but AFSS knows nothing about the taxiway closure leading to your hangar at your destination 900 miles away. To get L notams, you will need to call an FSS closer to home, either by radio en route or by phone before departure.

Abbreviated Briefing

This is the briefing you request when you're pacing the FBO's carpet waiting for the RVR to rise. You've already had your standard briefing, but found your destination to be W0X0F and you don't want to cancel the trip. Hoping for improvement, you call AFSS and say, "This is Comanche 1234P, I've already had a briefing; how's the weather at Furnace Springs?" Or, "I've had a standard briefing; what's the icing situation toward Lincoln?" The briefer will give you just what you need.

The abbreviated briefing is also a good tool for en route when you have 10 minutes to kill on a passenger drop. Call AFSS, "This is Comanche 34P, I'm at Frostbite Falls and I've had a standard briefing, may I have the weather for Duluth, please?" This same technique applies when calling flight service in flight. In fact, any service you receive from flight service on the telephone may be had airborne.

An AFSS may have 50 frequencies to monitor, ranging from VORs to in-flight communications frequencies. Despite the confusing array of little boxes on the en route charts explaining what frequency is appropriate, there is one frequency that works most of the time—122.2. If you're too busy trying to keep the airplane upright to look up a frequency, just dial it in (or keep one stored in that 99-memory radio you just bought) and call in the blind, "Mumble Radio, Cessna 123 on 122.2 over Pawnee City VOR."

Whichever flight service hears the call should answer. Give the same information you would on the telephone, and expect the same response. If the frequency sounds busy, however, you may wish to keep your requests short and save filing your next three flight plans until you're on the ground. Flight plan processing takes a fair amount of time and you could be blocking some other pilot desperately trying to get a weather update. Of course, the easiest method is to ask ATC—you're already talking to them—for the weather. We're happy to get, time permitting.

Flight Watch—122.0—is another option for getting updated weather but never use it for filing flight plans. If you're uncertain which AFSS handles Flight Watch, just dial in 122.0 and call, "Flight Watch, Cessna 123 over Moline." Then wait. The briefer will get to you in order. Each en route center has a Flight Watch associated with it. Chicago Center airspace is covered by Kankakee Flight Watch; Kansas City center by Columbia and so forth across country. On long flights, you may wish to monitor flight watch—without abandoning ATC—and listen to other pilots giving pireps. You may hear what you need without ever calling.

Who Briefs the Briefers?

In the tower/en route ATC world, position relief briefing responsibilities are mandated. Both the incoming and outgoing controllers share responsibilities to discuss both the traffic and weather situation. "...the specialist being relieved is obligated to provide a complete, accurate briefing and the relieving specialist is obligated to ensure that the briefing takes place and is to his/her total satisfaction."

Prior to ever stepping up to the position, controllers are required to perform a ritual self-briefing; much like FAR 91.103 requiring pilots to "...become familiar with all available information concerning that flight." In the tracon, there is a short checklist and status board of some sort listing outages and delays and anything else pertaining to the operation. The same applies to AFSS.

The flight service manual requires the controller coming on duty to go through all available information and get a good picture of the weather situation as well as traffic management programs in effect. This usually takes only a few minutes, then the relieving briefer is ready to work. With the AFSS stations covering much larger chunks of airspace than the old stations, a briefer really must be familiar with weather for the entire country and have a good idea where the traffic delays will be from coast to coast.

They don't memorize this information but if a Lear pilot calls for a briefing in Ohio and he wants weather for Arizona, the briefer should have a general idea of what's out there. While I was listening to Terry at FOD AFSS, a Westwind pilot called for a briefing from a small airport in northern Iowa. He was planning a trip to Concorde, California (CCR). While Terry hadn't heard of CCR, he had a good idea what was happening weather and flow-wise to the Bay area, and with a few keystrokes had all the specifics for the pilot including winds at flight levels for his entire route.

It helps to have all identifiers handy when speaking to flight service. It saves the briefer from looking them up for you. The Westwind pilot did it correctly, "I'm landing at Concorde—Charlie, Charlie Romeo."

Weather information is fed to AFSS from numerous sites including National Weather Service (NWS), AWOS and ASOS. All AFSSs should have access to the GOES (Geostationary Operational Environmental Satellite) satellite system. Only one satellite was on line when I was visiting, but the infrared pictures from outer space covered most of the country and were simply phenomenal. While the pilot can't see the images over the telephone, they do give the briefer great physical information or at least something neat to stare at.

The country is also covered by 135 radar sites—both NWS and ATC—that can provide current weather data to the briefer. Usually, the briefer has a picture of the local area out to about 180 miles. Calling up other sites anywhere in the country takes a few minutes as the data travels through various computers, digitizers, microwave ovens and whatelse. By asking the briefer to call up a radar site at the beginning of the briefing, he can make the request, give you the standard briefing and by the time it's complete, your radar data should be available.

IFR Flight Not Recommended

Anytime flight service gives a briefing containing a forecast of less than VFR minima—or if, in the briefer's opinion, the weather may take an unexpected turn for the worse, the briefer is required to tell a VFR pilot, "VFR flight not recommended." The go/no go decision is still the pilot's but should the flight end on a mountainside, AFSS is covered. But what about IFR planning? Will a briefer tell an instrument pilot, "IFR flight not recommended?" Yes, but not in so many words.

While the final decision to launch is always the pilot's, the flight service briefer may be aware of apocalyptically lousy weather en route and should wisely say to the Cessna 172 pilot, "Hey, I wouldn't recommend taking the plane out of the hangar." Usually, the more diplomatic question will be, "Can this flight be made eight hours from now?" Or, "Can you take a different route?"

If a thick-headed pilot insists upon boring into the teeth of a hurricane despite warnings from the briefer, you can be sure the briefer will give a most complete briefing, leaving no stone unturned. At that point, the briefer knows his or her actions may be replayed in a courtroom years after the funeral. As pilot, you should never be afraid to ask AFSS, "What do you think?" The briefer may dance around an exact opinion, but if your experience level is low and you've never flown IFR in the area, the second opinion could help.

Too often an overly sensitive ego can keep both pilots and controllers from admitting mistakes and asking for help. As a controller, I've more than once declined help only to demonstrate that I didn't have a firm grasp of the traffic situation. I make the same mistakes flying and once ignored an approaching thunderstorm and continued with a landing (in a taildragger) only to end up in the adjoining cornfield feeling very stupid.

Getting a briefing from flight service can be another opportunity to conceal ignorance and suffer the consequences. Once you've declared to the briefer, "I am an instrument pilot!" the briefer knows he's is not dealing with a 12-hour student and will assume you know certain things. Rapping off figures from the 850-millibar chart may sound to you like the USDA hog report and you'd be somewhat embarrassed to admit it. But that's *exactly* the time to admit, "Hey, what's that mean?" Look upon this as a chance to pick up some free ground instruction. Flight service people are often bored out of their skulls and would love the chance to both show off and do something a little different than reading weather over the telephone.

Unadvertised Services

In the old days, the flight service person—Ed—was also a licensed weather observer who would trudge into the snow and stare at the sky and say, "Damn cold out here."

Today, the AFSS not only doesn't take weather or give traffic advisories (with some exceptions) but they don't even have any windows. While I was at FOD AFSS, a snow storm moved in and I wasn't aware until I stepped outside. In the old days, Ed would stay up all night posting weather charts, recording broadcasts and taking weather observations. Today, the late night AFSS controller fights to stay awake waiting for the 5 a.m. rush. Weather is automatically updated. The hourly HIWAS recording breaks the monotony or a call from an outlying weather observer kills two minutes, but automation has removed much of the romance (and aviation) from flight service. Frankly, many flight service people, particularly the older ones, long for the chance to do something. Two a.m. is a great time to visit or call and ask, "Hey, I couldn't sleep; you got time for a question?" You can clear up anything you ever misunderstood about flight service or other aspects of flying the system. And it's free. (Sort of.)

• Section Four •

Decisions
in the
Cockpit

At
Takeoff

I n this section we'll examine in detail some scenarios in which making timely and correct decisions is essential. We'll take it by phase of flight,
beginning here with the takeoff.
Some of these decisions are critical to your survival,while others are less so. For
example, engine failure in a piston twin close to the ground is a dire emergency.
The same failure at cruise over flat terrain is much less of one, and so the
decisions the pilot must make are different.
We'll start with another accident report, this one having to do with engine
failure at takeoff. As we'll see, in some cases the critical point is that a decision
be made in time, regardless of what it is.

Fatal Indecision

Pilots pay a high price for the extra performance and systems redundancy provided by piston twins. The payment we're concerned with
here is not in the form of hard dollars. It's a levy imposed by the
possibility of an engine failure at the worst possible time: on takeoff.

The currency is skill and judgment. The labor is maintaining control
and exploiting the meager performance that's still available to bring
the flight to a safe conclusion.

Records show that one in every 10 accidents involving piston twins
occurs when pilots are unable to pay the price. There's no doubt that
an engine failure on takeoff is one of aviation's toughest challenges.
Loss of control is the penalty for any delay in response or flaw in pilot
technique.

Those who would assume that such mishaps befall the inexperienced will be surprised to learn that they typically involve pilots with thousands of hours of flying experience and hundreds of hours in type.

Furthermore, accident reports often reveal that pilots react improperly—or not at all—to engine failures in piston twins. In many cases, airspeed is allowed to decay until control is lost and the airplane rolls inverted. Landing gear and flaps are left extended. The propeller on the "dead" engine is left windmilling. In haste or confusion, the wrong engine is shut down.

Such an accident occurred several years ago, and the results of the investigation provide a few clues about why experienced multi-engine pilots sometimes do not respond successfully to the challenge of an engine failure on takeoff.

The airplane, a Piper Chieftain, was a commuter airline workhorse. The pilots were experienced. Both were ATPs in their early 30s. The captain had done a lot of multi-engine instruction before joining the airline. Nearly a third of his 4,300 hours of flight time were in piston twins. His experience included more than 800 hours in Chieftains.

In the right seat was a new-hire who was being groomed to become a captain for the commuter. The "captain-trainee" was along on this flight just to observe, learn the routes and help the captain with baggage. He had been assigned no copilot duties. A former instructor and examiner in Air Force C-141s, the pilot had flown most of his 3,250 hours in multi-engine jets. But he had no previous experience in light piston twins.

Behind Schedule

Delays during the three trips the crew already had flown had put them well behind schedule when the Chieftain landed at Houston's William P. Hobby Airport shortly after 7 p.m. The airplane was late for its scheduled departure to Brownsville, Texas. The weather was clear and the temperature was 56° F.

Perhaps hurrying to make up some time, the captain used his company's fudge factors of 165 pounds for each passenger and 170 pounds for each crew member in preparing the load manifest. His calculations indicated that with two pilots, eight passengers and baggage, the Chieftain would be right at its maximum gross weight of 7,000 pounds and its aft c.g. limit of 135 inches. He did so, even though several of the occupants obviously weighed much more than the FAA-approved limits. Indeed, four of the passengers and the captain, himself, weighed more than 200 pounds.

According to calculations by the National Transportation Safety Board, the Chieftain actually was 280 pounds over max gross and its c.g.

was three inches behind the aft limit. However, the board determined that the extra weight would not have affected the Chieftain's single-engine performance to any great extent. It noted that the tendency of the airplane to yaw into the failed engine would have been more pronounced than normal due to the aft c.g. The captain, who was flying the aircraft, would have needed to apply more rudder pressure than normal during such an emergency to counteract the asymmetric yaw.

Thirty minutes after landing in Houston, the Chieftain began taxiing out for takeoff with its new load of passengers and baggage bound for Brownsville. It was Eagle Commuter Airlines Flight 108.

No Run-up

The Chieftain was promptly cleared into position and to hold on Hobby's Runway 22. After waiting a couple of minutes on the runway, Flight 108 was cleared to take off.

Another pilot, who was waiting to depart on Runway 22 at the time, recalled that the Chieftain had not used the run-up area. The pilot also said it appeared that the crew never performed a preflight check of the Chieftain's engines.

The tower controller apparently noticed that the Chieftain began banking at about 100 feet. The controller asked the crew if they would be making a right turn away from the airport. The response, by the captain-trainee, was: "Eagle 108 just lost the right engine."

According to NTSB's reconstruction of the takeoff, the Chieftain was 90 feet above the runway when it lost power from the right engine, a 350-horsepower Lycoming TIO-540J. The landing gear had been retracted, but the flaps were still at the 15-degree takeoff setting.

Indicated airspeed was at or just below 109 knots, the published best single-engine rate of climb speed (Vyse). At that speed, the airplane had a 30-knot buffer above its minimum single-engine control speed (Vmc).

Decision Time

The emergency procedures section of the Chieftain manual provides two options: "If engine failure occurs when sufficient airspeed above Vmc is obtained, the pilot must decide whether to abort the takeoff or attempt a single-engine takeoff. His decision should be based on his judgment, considering the runway remaining, density altitude, loading, obstructions, weather and his own capability."

NTSB's opinion is that aborting the takeoff and landing straight ahead would have been the better option. There was sufficient room to do so. Runway 22 at Hobby is 7,600 feet long and has a flat, 1,300-foot clear zone off the end that is obstructed only by approach lights. The board said if the crew had reduced power on the left engine, lowered the gear and dropped the flaps to their full, 40-degrees extension, they probably could have been able to bring the Chieftain to a stop with minimum damage. They would have used up all of the remaining runway and about half of the clear area.

Lesser Option

The crew also could have tried to continue flying. But that option would have been more difficult and risky. Configuring the airplane to stay in the air would have entailed nearly a dozen tasks that would have had to be performed promptly, flawlessly and from memory.

The first task would have been to maintain adequate airspeed—Vyse, 109 knots. The Chieftain was either at or slightly below this speed when the right engine failed. With the drag from the windmilling propeller and the flaps, the airplane would have been losing precious airspeed at this point. The pilots would have had to put the nose down immediately and start a shallow descent to regain and maintain 109 knots.

The crew would have had to ensure that the mixture, prop and throttle controls were full forward, and that the landing gear was retracted. They would then retract the flaps, identify the "dead" engine and verify the choice by retarding the throttle. The prop on the failed engine would have to be feathered, the mixture set to idle/cut-off and the airplane banked about five degrees into the good engine to reduce drag.

With these tasks accomplished, the Chieftain might have been able to stay in the air. Single-engine rate of climb in the over-gross condition would have been about 190 fpm, at most, according to NTSB.

What Now?

As mentioned earlier, the board believes a decision to land straight ahead would have better than trying to keep the airplane flying so close to the ground and at night.

What decision did the pilots make? Incredibly, the evidence points to the conclusion that the crew did very little in response to the engine failure.

Survivors recalled hearing an engine surging and popping, and felt the airplane begin veering to the right. Two of them heard one of the pilots say something to the effect of, "What do we do now?"

After the captain-trainee reported the engine failure, the Chieftain maintained runway heading for about 10 seconds before beginning a right turn and a shallow descent. The turn and descent rate steepened.

The wings were leveled just before the Chieftain crashed on a parking ramp, 90 degrees off runway heading. It slid into two other airplanes, four vehicles and a hangar.

Three passengers survived with serious injuries. The other five occupants were killed. No one on the ground was hurt.

Probable Cause

The engine failure at a critical moment during the takeoff and the Chieftain's "marginal" single-engine performance capability were ascribed as probable causes of the crash. The cause of the engine failure was never determined, due to extensive fire damage.

NTSB also faulted the captain's incorrect reponse to the emergency—that is, his failure either to land on the remaining runway or configure the piston twin to sustain single-engine flight.

The Chieftain crashed with its flaps still extended 15 degrees. And the propeller on the *left* engine had been feathered. (The right engine had failed.)

Considering the captain's extensive experience as a multi-engine instructor, he should have been able to handle the emergency. NTSB proposed one possible explanation of why he had not been: "Apparently, the captain was not mentally prepared to analyze and respond to the engine failure."

Seeking a Thread

Beyond this rather tentative conclusion, the investigation revealed very little about the human factors aspects of this accident.

There was no examination of what may have been the captain's physical and mental state. And the possible interactions between the captain and the "captain-trainee," who had not yet received company training and was along just to observe, went wholly unexplored.

Someday, human factors research may provide us with a clearer understanding of why such mistakes are made repeatedly by otherwise well-trained and experienced pilots. In the meantime, we suspect that what NTSB postulated about the Chieftain captain's lack of mental preparation may be a prominent factor in this type of mishap.

It's not just the complacency that tends to take root in a pilot's psyche after dozens, perhaps hundreds of uneventful takeoffs. Or the comforting defense mechanism that lulls a pilot into thinking that engine failures are rare and happen only to "other guys."

We suspect that what's also involved here is the inability of even the best initial and recurrent multi-engine training to prepare a pilot to act *instinctively* to an engine failure on takeoff.

There are tough choices to make, complex procedures to follow and very little time in which to react.

Mental preparation is the key. An engine failure has to be expected and planned for. Emergency procedures that must be performed from memory must be mentally rehearsed.

Then, and only then, may the pilot be confident that he or she is ready to meet the challenge of taking off in a piston twin.

Let's take another look at risk management, this time as it applies to takeoffs.

While one might think that engine failure is the number-one danger at takeoff, simple loss of control of the airplane also brings many pilots to grief.

Managing Takeoff Risks

What can we, as pilots, do to prevent a mishap on takeoff or, at least, give ourselves the best chance of surviving a mishap if one occurs?

The last part of the question is important, because things *are* going to happen over which we have little or no control. It is important to anticipate and prepare for emergencies ahead of time, both emotionally and intellectually, because correct and timely response is critical. On takeoff, things happen fast, close to the ground, where there is little time to sort out what is happening and make decisions.

Risk management begins by ensuring that we don't "put ourselves in a box"—that we don't *do it to ourselves* because of something we did or didn't do, or because we were psychologically unprepared for those random, unavoidable events that challenge our preparation and proficiency. On takeoff, as in any phase of flight, the best way to handle risk is to avoid it. As pilots, we must avoid placing ourselves in situations with few good solutions.

The bottom line is, however, that we *are* doing it to ourselves. The overwhelming majority of the takeoff accidents during the most recent two-year period for which reports were available involved loss of power and/or loss of control. These accidents are avoidable. If we would just take steps to maintain control of the aircraft and keep the engine from losing power, we would probably reduce our chances of being involved in a takeoff accident by 90 percent or more.

Head in the Game

A reasonable first step is to develop a consciousness of everything that could adversely affect aircraft control and power production, and to focus on these factors when we begin thinking about a flight, while planning for that flight and during preflight, taxi, run-up and takeoff.

The next step is to ask questions—about ourselves, our aircraft and the flying environment. Flight instructors can help, not only to provide answers, but to make sure that we are asking the *right* questions and critically evaluating ourselves, our environment and our aircraft.

We should accept the fact that, like all other human beings, pilots do make mistakes, and we should be especially alert for our own mistakes. We can minimize our chances for error by *thinking* about what we are doing, all the time. We have to "keep our heads in the game." If you find that tough to do on a given day, don't fly.

Consider the following report from the two-year sample: A Piper Saratoga struck a lighted generator on the runway during a night takeoff at John Wayne Airport in California. The generator had been put there to illuminate the X indicating that the runway was closed. The obstacle was mentioned in the ATIS broadcast, but the pilot said he "heard what he expected to hear when he listened to ATIS." Clearly, his head wasn't in the game.

We can only wonder what another pilot was thinking when his Cessna U-206 seaplane crashed after a couple of attempts to take off from a lake with a four-by-four and a ball of concrete still attached to its tail.

Risk management apparently was a low priority of a student pilot who made an off-airport landing in his ski-equipped Piper PA-11 so that *his passenger* could photograph a bear. The right landing gear collapsed when the ski impacted a snowbank on takeoff. Material failure was *not* listed as the cause of the accident.

Then there's the pilot who attempted to take off with the fuel selector positioned on an empty tank.

There's also the J-3 Cub that would have been over gross with the 230-pound pilot, the 190-pound passenger and more than four gallons of fuel. It crashed on takeoff from a small grass strip, killing both occupants.

It would be easy to read these stories and say, "That would never happen to me." Well, maybe not, *if* you keep your head in the game.

Losing Control

Now, let's look specifically at the two main causes of mishap on takeoff and initial climb: loss of aircraft control and loss of engine power. Then we'll take a look at how to avoid them.

There are many "bad actors" in the grand drama of aircraft control loss: wind, density altitude, poor runway or surface conditions, flight control problems and material failure. Lack of ability to fly the airplane or handle the circumstances, and lack of training, discipline and proficiency also appear on the list of players.

Material failure is probably the pilot's greatest nightmare. We all have read of mixture controls coming out of the instrument panel and throttle linkages breaking and leaving the engine at full or idle power. One accident report in our sample read as follows: "The flight instructor and the student pilot were practicing touch-and-go landings. Despite emergency procedures, the engine power would not increase, and a forced landing was made in a residential area. During the descent, the airplane impacted wires and a traffic light pole. Post-accident inspection revealed the throttle arm had fallen off the carburetor shaft. The unit had not been saftied (sic) in place." Short of an uncowled, physical inspection, there is *no way* the problem could have been anticipated by the pilots. They handled the emergency well, however; there were no injuries.

If it's been a while since you've done stalls, why not take a few minutes to see how they feel...and sound. Refamiliarization could make the difference in that split second after takeoff when an otherwise inconsequential distraction or warning light could cause a departure stall at low altitude. The dividends from stall awareness practice can be dramatic.

Tough Environment

NTSB's records show that many control-loss accidents occur when takeoffs are attempted with tailwinds, excessive crosswinds or known wind shear, or from runways with tall wet grass, soft sod or hidden holes.

Consider this account of a Piper Arrow that departed from Angel Fire, N.M. in March 1989: "The takeoff was made on Runway 35 with a density altitude calculated to be 10,645 feet. The local winds were reported to be from 270 degrees at 25 knots with gusts to 30 knots. The aircraft gained 300 feet, but the turn to crosswind resulted in an altitude loss. The pilot stated he could not maintain altitude and executed an off-airport precautionary landing with the gear up. The airport fixed base operator stated several aircraft abandoned landings and diverted to other airports due to turbulence and high wind." This pilot voluntarily entered a hazardous environment in which he lost aircraft control.

Loss of power, what most of us call engine failure, also has a long list of potential causes, including: fuel starvation, carburetor ice, ignition failure and fuel contamination.

Adequate planning and preflight procedures can reduce the risk of a power loss on takeoff. Simply validating that our procedures are

complete and then following them in a disciplined way can immeasur-
ably enhance our chances of eliminating power loss as a problem on
departure.

Among the hundreds of reports involving power loss in our two-
year sample were two which show that June 17, 1989 wasn't a very good
day for exhaust valves. As with many accidents, however, material
failure was only part of the story. The report on the Cessna 421 that
crashed in Arizona notes that density altitude was three and a half times
the field elevation of 1,600 feet. The outside air temperature was 114
degrees. Operating conditions like that should raise a lot of red flags,
even for pilots who are accustomed to the Southwest heat. The pilot
apparently responded correctly to the engine failure, but the big piston
twin was unable to stay airborne on the remaining engine. Careful
preflight planning and particular attention to performance charts are
critical in conditions where aircraft performance may be marginal. The
wisest choice might be *not to go* when performance on a single engine
is shaky.

The other accident involved a Cessna 150 that was 10 hours past due
for a 100-hour inspection. The student pilot noticed an excessive mag
drop on run-up and no airspeed indication until the airplane was
halfway down the runway. She aborted, but too late; skid marks did not
begin until 3,300 feet from the start of the takeoff roll on the 3,500-foot
runway. Something was clearly wrong with the airplane before this
accident happened.

This story should provoke an evaluation of our own abort criteria.
We should ensure that we have psychologically conditioned ourselves
to abort as readily as to fly.

Avoiding Obstacles

Another leading cause of takeoff accidents is simply labeled as "collision with object." If it's "out there," airplanes have collided with it.
Trees, soft spots in sod fields, snow mounds, earthen berms, fences,
power lines and so on. The reports reveal that the pilots who hit these
objects were generally unaware that they were there.

We should review the notams and check out a current edition of the
Airport/Facilities Directory for information on obstacles. If we're landing
at an unfamiliar airport, why not look around while flying the pattern
to identify potential obstructions so that we can plan for departure
emergencies?

On cross-country flights, I make an effort to "scope out" airfields in
this manner. This practice can help us to formulate reasonable, work-
able "bail-out plans" for almost every airfield we use. Under certain

wind conditions, there are no good alternatives because of terrain or tree growth, but at least we can evaluate what we will face on departure from a particular runway and can be alert to abort at the earliest sign of trouble.

A walk around your local airfield is also recommended to see what's "out there" that could cause problems.

I remember the day, over 30 years ago, when I started making an effort to familiarize myself with the airfields on which I operate. I saw a takeoff turn into disaster for a large military aircraft filled with fuel and crew. There was a deep ditch on one side of the runway. Terrain on the other side of the runway was smooth and unobstructed. The aircraft departed the runway on the wrong side, broke apart and exploded.

A similar, but less tragic case involved a Cessna 150 pilot who recently took off from a narrow gravel road with an 18-knot *tail* wind. The aircraft had difficulty climbing and struck a tree.

Another pilot took off when density altitude was in excess of 11,500 feet, with a tailwind and facing upsloping terrain. He didn't make it. Small wonder there was a "collision with object."

The accident record cannot tell us how many pilots squeezed by on takeoff attempts under similar conditions. Perhaps they were just lucky. But luck, if there is such a thing, is fickle. We can profit from a comment by golf pro Jack Nicklaus, who said, "The more I practice, the luckier I get."

Setting Limits

If you believe that once basic proficiency is achieved, flying is over 90 percent "head" and less than 10 percent "hands," the lesson is to *think* much more about flying than we actually fly. Again, it's called "keeping our heads in the game."

We would like to think that pilots don't consciously fly in conditions that will cause us to lose control or that will significantly degrade aircraft performance, but the record shows that some of us neglect to take aggressive action to find out what's "out there," disregard adverse conditions or overestimate our proficiency to deal with threatening circumstances and events.

Knowing the challenges that we will face in flight begins with a good weather briefing and a check of legal and personal minimums and limits against existing conditions. No pilot should knowingly fly into dangerous or marginal conditions for any reason. No flight is that important.

If your engine is carbureted, a good weather check should always include computation of relative humidity to alert against possible carburetor icing. The carb heat check on run-up should involve more than manipulation of the handle and confirmation of an rpm drop. Keep the heat on for a moment and watch for an increase in rpm, which would indicate that you already had ice in the carburetor.

Carburetor icing probability charts show that icing is possible at temperatures exceeding 100 F and relative humidities as low as 20 percent, depending on the phase of flight.

Prior to every flight, it's also a good idea to determine when the next required inspections are due, as well as required system inspections (pitot/static, transponder, etc.). Discrepancies (i.e., the "squawk" sheet) also should be checked.

A good preflight, using the checklist, is extremely important. Conscious awareness of wind direction and velocity is an integral part of the walk-around, and the information obtained should be compared with what Flight Service thinks the winds are.

A visual check of fuel in all tanks for clarity and quantity is absolutely essential. The quantity seen should be compared against the gauge readings. Controls warrant an especially careful inspection, along with their attachments, freedom and correct movement.

Forewarned, Forearmed

ATIS, AWOS and personal observations need to be incorporated in our personal pre-launch conditioning. The attitude that "today is the day when the engine will quit" helps to promote the strong attention to preparation we need even for a "routine" flight. Forewarned is *really* forearmed.

Complete familiarity with departures and approaches at your home airfield and a check of the same items at en route fields can avert trauma should the unexpected happen.

There have been too many tragic attempts to return to the airfield after a power loss at low altitude on takeoff, when nearly ideal landing areas were available within 90 degrees of the runway heading. Knowledge, even of poor departure terrain, can be used to great advantage. If it is known that good emergency landing areas are not available for a particular runway, others may be selected, assuming a tailwind departure is not required.

If a good landing area isn't available, full attention should be applied to ensuring safe speed, maintenance of firm aircraft control and a touchdown that provides optimum chance of a successful off-airport landing.

Whatever the cause, if an engine failure occurs immediately after takeoff, get the nose down to establish the recommended glide speed and maintain absolute control of the aircraft to touchdown. Time permitting, other things need to be done, but not at the expense of flying speed and control.

Before advancing the power, I like to think I have done everything I can to prevent engine failure and loss of control. I consciously try to check out the airplane, the environment and myself very well *before* flight.

Being mentally prepared is what *really* counts. If we fly airplanes long enough, the day may come when an engine quits, regardless of what we've done "up front." We shouldn't be surprised at that. We should be ready for it. Circumstances may, at some time or another, cause us to partially or completely lose control of an aircraft. Thinking about that and being psychologically reconciled to the possibility will make better aviators of us all.

When the fateful day comes, the least we can say is that we have thought about it and disciplined ourselves and our procedures to try to prevent it from happening. If we are psychologically prepared and have done our homework—and if our proficiency is up to the standards of the certificates and ratings we hold—the outcome will be as good as we can possibly make it.

Flying a wounded twin just after takeoff is one of the most dangerous things a private pilot can do.

While we've discussed the handling of twins flying on one engine in previous volumes, it bears another look.

Twins: The Ragged Edge

The year 1979 was an eye-opener for multi-engine pilots. It was the year in which a special study of light twin engine-failure accidents was published by the National Transportation Safety Board. The study was a landmark in general aviation history because it shattered a myth.

Up to that time, many pilots assumed that multi-engine flying was patently safer than relying on a single engine. But the NTSB report established incontrovertible evidence to the contrary.

By studying scores of accidents, then crunching the numbers on such variables as power loading, cruise speeds, stall speeds and gross weight, the board proved just how unforgiving light twins can be when ill-prepared pilots are faced with the sudden loss of an engine's power in certain critical phases of flight.

Of the 2,229 accidents studied in the report, 610 involved fatalities.

Among the fatal accidents were 123 that resulted from engine failures. In nearly three-quarters of these cases, pilots lost control of their airplanes after the asymmetric thrust created by the engines that remained operating proved to be overwhelming.

The board extrapolated and came up with a disturbing discovery: The percentage of fatal accidents involving engine failure was more than four times greater in light twins than in single-engine aircraft.

Safer in a Single

The word soon spread. If you lost an engine, you were much safer gliding in a single than trying to cope with single-engine flying in a light twin. A spate of magazine articles and FAA publications soon followed, each one emphasizing the shortcomings of relying too heavily on a light twin's single-engine performance.

But since that time, we've seen relatively little emphasis by the media or government on the safety considerations of light-twin flying.

Efforts by aircraft manufacturers to make twins safer have been few and far between. One notable example was Cessna's development of the Skymaster, which has two engines mounted in tandem (asymmetric thrust is eliminated because all thrust is directed along the fuselage's centerline). While it might have been an engineering success, the Skymaster was, ultimately, a flop in the marketplace.

Another attempt to improve light twin safety was Piper's introduction of counter-rotating propellers in 1969. As we'll learn in a moment, counter-rotating propellers help to significantly reduce asymmetries of thrust should an engine failure occur.

Lower Redlines

By the late 1970s, the only light twins still being manufactured—the Piper Seminole and the Beechcraft Duchess—featured not just counter-rotating propellers, but remarkably low Vmcs, or single-engine, minimum-control airspeeds.

The Seminole's Vmc is 56 knots, just one knot higher than Vso (stall speed in landing configuration). The idea here is to prevent the pilot from entering into a dangerously slow, asymmetric condition by trying to ensure that conventional stall warnings occur before Vmc is reached.

The Seminole and Duchess also have relatively good single-engine climb capability, assuming flawless pilot technique and benign density altitude. Still, twins with these safety features are *not* immune from a Vmc-induced loss of control.

Today, the market for new light twins has virtually dried up, and existing light twins are aging rapidly. Some of them have the safety features mentioned above, but many, many others do not. As the allure of flying a twin shows no sign of fading, the warnings about flight near Vmc bear repeating.

Asymmetric Thrust

At the heart of the problem is the configuration of the conventional light twin. An engine on each wing guarantees asymmetric thrust should one engine lose power or fail entirely. In twins with both engines rotating clockwise, further asymmetries are realized. That's because, as we all learned in our earliest student days, a propeller's descending blades produce more thrust by virtue of their higher angle of attack.

Take a look at Figure 1, which is a representation of a conventional light twin, with propellers that both rotate in a clockwise direction. The illustration shows the descending propeller blades' increased thrust vectors. Note that both are to the right of each engine, but note also how much farther the right propeller's high-thrust zone is from the airplane's c.g.

Question: In the event of an engine failure, which engine's loss would create the most asymmetric thrust? Answer: The left engine, because its propeller's high-thrust vector is close to the center of gravity. The right propeller's descending blades are comparatively far from the c.g., so the moment they create is greater. Lose the left engine in this type of twin, and the yaw to the left will be powerful indeed. Much more powerful than the yawing moment should the right engine have failed.

Critical Engine

That's why the left engine on a conventional twin is termed the critical engine in aerodynamic parlance. Twins with counter-rotating propellers don't have a critical engine; both propellers rotate towards (or on some aircraft, such as the Piper Aerostar 700P, away from) the fuselage, and the thrust vectors are the same distance from the center of gravity.

Whether you have conventional or counter-rotating propellers, the method for stopping the yaw towards a dead engine is the same. Apply rudder pressure opposite the direction of the yaw. If in doubt, stomp on the rudder pedal offering the most resistance.

Incidentally, this helps you identify which engine has lost power—the "dead" foot marks the ailing engine. The inclinometer can also help identify a power loss; the rudder ball will move away from the bad engine.

But the rudder's effectiveness depends on airspeed. As long as your airspeed is high enough, rudder pressure will stop the yawing moment. Allow it to dissipate, however, and the yaw can't be stopped. The aircraft can go out of control and enter a roll toward the failed engine. If the failed engine's wing enters a stall, the result can be a spin in the direction of the dead engine—often an inverted spin from which recovery will be impossible.

Danger Zone

Vmc, marked by a red radial line on the airspeed indicator, delineates the danger zone. Lose an engine at or below this airspeed, and you will not have enough rudder power to overcome the asymmetric yaw.

By regulation, manufacturers must determine Vmc by duplicating a certain configuration during flight tests. This configuration includes:
- A windmilling—or unfeathered—propeller on the dead engine.
- Takeoff or maximum continuous power on the operating engine.
- Landing gear retracted. When landing gear are extended, they act like miniature rudders and help to stabilize the flight path. When they are retracted, drag is reduced and asymmetric thrust effects are increased.
- Flaps at the takeoff setting.
- Maximum takeoff weight.
- Most aft center of gravity.
- Establishment of zero-sideslip toward the operating engine.
- Standard atmospheric conditions.

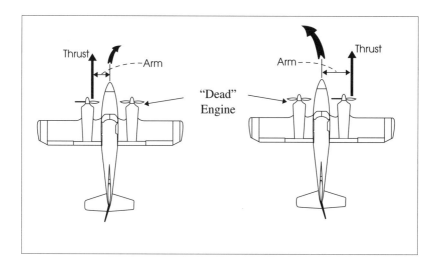

The idea behind the rule to quantify Vmc is simple: Provide a speed that pilots can use as a reference for gauging their proximity to one of aviation's most dangerous flight envelopes. It has special significance during the takeoff phase, when airspeeds are low, angles of attack are high, altitude is at a premium and any loss of power will be attended by swift loss of precious airspeed. The closer you are to Vmc during takeoff, the more you risk.

It is especially important for pilots to make sure that Vmc is exceeded by at least five knots before rotating the nose wheel on the takeoff roll. Once airborne, no time should be wasted in accelerating to the airplane's best single-engine rate of climb speed (Vyse) or best single-engine angle of climb speed (Vxse).

Vmc Changes

Too often, pilots get the idea that Vmc is a static number, one that never varies. Wrong. There are a number of variables that can make a twin's *real* Vmc higher or lower than the value published in the pilot's operating handbook and the number appearing at the redline on the airspeed indicator. Those are textbook numbers.

Modify any of the variables that define the flight-test version of Vmc and you have a new number. How often do standard conditions prevail? How quickly can you react to a power loss and identify, verify and feather a failed engine, and establish zero-sideslip? How often will the airplane be loaded to its most aft c.g.?

The answers, most likely, are: never; slowly; and not very often. So in real life, Vmc will not be accurately represented by the value on the airspeed indicator.

Let's look at how deviations from textbook Vmc can occur, with

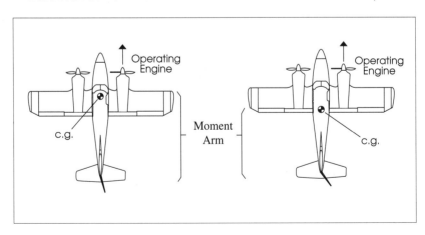

special attention to higher-than-published Vmcs. High Vmcs are worse because a larger portion of the aircraft's flight envelope is exposed to the risk of uncontrollable yaw and roll. Vmc will be higher than the published speed whenever the following conditions prevail:

• At low gross weights, because the yawing moment is stronger when there is less mass to propel.

• At higher angles of attack, because of a higher drag profile. This means a swifter loss of airspeed at the moment of engine failure.

• Out of ground effect, where drag is higher.

• Low density altitude. Engines produce more thrust in denser air, so asymmetric thrust is greater when an engine loses power. Conversely, high density altitudes lower Vmc because propellers don't produce as much thrust in thinner air.

• In a sideslip.

"Raise the Dead"

It used to be that instructors taught their multi-engine students to center the inclinometer's rudder ball as a part of configuring a twin for single-engine flight.

No more. Rudder deflection and frontal drag are at a maximum when holding a wings-level attitude with the ball centered. In this configuration, Vmc can rise by as much as 15 knots over the published value, and the chances of a single-engine climb can be nullified altogether.

For best performance, use just enough rudder pressure to keep the rudder ball between one-half and three-quarters of its width out of the center position, towards the operating engine.

In addition, establish a five-degree bank into the operating engine (or "raise the dead," as some instructors say). This will produce the low-drag, zero-sideslip configuration.

Unlike some of the above effects, the immense drag of an unfeathered, windmilling propeller is easy to visualize. Just think of all the energy you can spend while turning a propeller by hand. Airborne, the relative wind encounters just as much resistance, for two reasons. Unfeathered propeller blades present more surface area to the relative wind, and the windmilling takes place at the expense of fighting the compression strokes in each of the engine's cylinders.

The effect of an aft c.g. is best understood by looking at the second figure. Compare the arms running between the rudder and the center of gravity depictions. With an aft c.g., there is a less powerful moment arm and less available rudder power for counteracting yaw and roll motions.

One important fact to keep in mind when practicing Vmc demonstrations is that at altitude, Vmc decreases because of thinner air and a consequent loss of thrust. But an airplane's stall speed remains the same. At some given altitude, a light twin's Vmc and stall speed will converge. A practice Vmc demonstration at too high an altitude can turn into a disaster, because the airplane may begin its uncontrolled yawing at the same moment it stalls. To avoid this, many instructors limit their Vmc work to density altitudes at or below 4,000 feet. Check with your instructor to see how he deals with this situation.

No Margin for Error

Like any other aspect of pilot skill, the avoidance of flight near Vmc and the successful management of an engine failure in a light twin require the kind of proficiency that can only come from practice.

Pilots of light twins should make it their business to have dual instruction in single-engine emergencies at least twice a year. That's the time to hone your skills at identifying, verifying, feathering, establishing zero sideslip and maintaining the proper single-engine airspeeds.

Just bear in mind that a twin with an engine out loses 80 percent of its total climb performance, not 50 percent. And even the remaining marginal capability depends on the pilot performing all emergency procedures flawlessly. Fail to retract the landing gear, feather the propeller of the failed engine, hold Vyse or Vxse, or maintain a zero-sideslip condition, and the airplane will not climb at all.

It will descend.

Okay, you're on the runway and rolling. Before you climb away from the runway, you have a big problem.

How do you deal with it? One of the tricky things about departure is that the environment the airplane is in changes rapidly from static to moving to airborne. An emergency at any one stage may require a different decision from the pilot than one at another stage.

Of course, the larger and heavier the airplane, the greater the consequences of an aborted takeoff. Here we have some words on how to deal with one when and if it does occur.

To Stop or Not to Stop

Consider the following situation: It's a fine day for flying. Winds are light. No clouds. The airport isn't very busy. You are just itching to get into the air. You line up on the active in your standard 12-year-old single. The runway is 2,500 feet long, paved, with a short overrun and a housing development off the departure end. Density altitude is 4,000 feet.

You advance the throttle and begin to roll. Initially, everything seems normal. Acceleration is good. All the instruments are in the green. The engine sounds nice and strong. At 30 knots, you notice a slight vibration coming from the front of the airplane, and it increases rapidly to a pronounced shimmy. As you accelerate through 40 knots, it gets worse.

What now? You quickly run through the possibilities and try to decide what to do. Should you keep going? Try to stop? What about the flight you had planned? By 50 knots, you already have used up one-third of the available runway, and the remaining asphalt is disappearing at the rate of 85 feet each second.

The aircraft begins to shake violently, so badly that you decide you had better abort. What did the POH say about aborting a takeoff on the runway? Maintain control, retard throttle, apply maximum braking, stop on the paved surface. You manage to do all these things, and the aircraft comes to a stop 400 feet from the end of the runway.

What happened? In this case, my nose gear shimmy damper had failed and separated from the strut, producing an intense, velocity-sensitive vibration in the front end of the Cessna 172RG. The only outcome, other than the needed repair, was a somewhat unnerved pilot.

The situation was manageable and not really all that serious, but it did start me thinking about rejected takeoffs (RTOs).

How many pilots actively consider, *before* they start to roll, the possibility of aborting a takeoff? Aircraft flight manuals don't devote much space to discussing it.

There is very little information elsewhere that directly relates to RTOs in general aviation aircraft, although there is a ton of material that applies to air carriers.

Airline Experience

RTOs are not uncommon in the air carrier world. They happen on the average about once in every 2,000 takeoffs. Most are precipitated by engine or system failures (or indications of failure), or problems with landing gear or tires.

Most RTOs are completed successfully, but once in a while the outcome is an accident. Almost all of the accidents involve an attempted RTO at or above V_1, resulting in a high-kinetic-energy event which goes wrong.

V_1 is the "decision speed" or "critical engine failure speed." It is the calculated indicated airspeed from which the airplane can either stop on the available runway or take off safely following failure of the critical engine using only aerodynamic forces and "average" pilot skills.

It is usually operationally applied as the velocity at which a decision *must* be reached and action taken to continue or stop if any emergency occurs which might jeopardize the flight.

V_1 is determined by a variety of factors, including aircraft weight and performance, pavement surface, runway length and pilot reaction times. The RTO capability of any new air carrier aircraft must be demonstrated during the certification process and tested per FAR 25.

The speeds relative to RTOs come from laboratory testing by test pilots who expect to have to stop, on dry pavement, with a new aircraft. As we shall see, most RTOs don't happen under those conditions.

V_1 and RTO also are part of a concept called "balanced field length," the theoretical distance in which a specific aircraft can accelerate to V_1 and *either* be brought to a stop with a maximum-effort abort *or* coaxed to an altitude of 35 feet should the pilot elect to continue the takeoff.

Balanced field length, in effect, determines the *minimum* runway length required for a specific aircraft to operate at a specific weight. It also dictates the *maximum* gross takeoff weight for a specific aircraft on a particular runway.

The procedures for RTOs are fairly simple. If a problem occurs before reaching V_1, the pilot should apply the abort procedures. If something happens above V_1, the pilot should continue the takeoff and deal with the problem afterwards.

Late on the Binders

The record shows that most airline RTO accidents occur when an abort is attempted at or beyond V_1.

The decision to abort results in an overrun or other departure from the paved surface, often with subsequent landing gear failure and major damage to the aircraft. Most injuries result from post-crash fire or evacuation difficulties.

In many of these cases, had the takeoff been continued, the outcome would likely have been much less severe.

Another common factor in most RTO accidents is that they occurred in other than ideal conditions. The runways were short, wet or slick. Aircraft equipment was in less-than-ideal mechanical condition. The crew was distracted.

Let's take a look at some specific accidents:
- In 1978, a Continental DC-10 overran the departure end of the

runway at Los Angeles following a rejected takeoff. The RTO was initiated near V_1 because the flight crew heard a loud metallic "bang" and the aircraft began to "quiver." The aircraft departed the wet paved surface, the left main landing gear collapsed, and fire erupted on the left side of the aircraft.

The DC-10 came to rest 664 feet from the departure end of the runway. Of the 186 passengers and 14 crew members, 31 were seriously injured and two were killed.

NTSB determined that the probable cause was the sequential failure of two tires on the left main gear and the resultant failure of a third tire on the same gear at a critical time during the takeoff roll.

The captain's attempt to reject the takeoff was hindered by reduced braking action due to the blown tires and the wet runway surface.

• In 1979, a Spantax DC-10 with 379 passengers and 13 crew ran off a runway at Malaga, Spain when the captain aborted the takeoff at or slightly above V_1 due to a strong airframe vibration. After running off the end of the 10,500-foot runway, the aircraft struck a concrete ILS building. Fire broke out in the right wing as fuel spilled out. Fifty passengers and three flight attendants were killed by the fire, and many other occupants were injured.

The investigation revealed that a nose gear tire had failed 6,000 feet from the beginning of the DC-10's takeoff roll.

• In 1985, a NASA Convair 990 was destroyed by fire after a rejected takeoff at March Air Force Base, California. The RTO was initiated just before V_1 when two tires on the right main landing gear exploded. During the roll-out, fragments of the tires or parts of associated brake assemblies punctured the right wing fuel tank.

Leaking fuel ignited, and the fire rapidly engulfed the four-engine airplane. The crew of four and their passengers, 15 scientists, successfully evacuated without any injury.

• In 1988, an American Airlines DC-10 ran off the end of the runway during a rejected takeoff at Dallas-Fort Worth. The RTO was initiated at V_1 following the sounding of a takeoff warning horn and illumination of a slat disagreement light.

The aircraft decelerated normally for the first few seconds, but the rate of deceleration then decreased and the aircraft left the runway at 97 knots. The nose gear collapsed in soft earth, and the DC-10 plowed to a stop 1,000 feet beyond the runway.

Of the 239 passengers and 15 crew, only the captain and flight engineer were seriously injured. Five occupants suffered minor injuries during the evacuation. There was no fire, but the aircraft was damaged beyond economic repair.

NTSB determined the probable cause to be the total failure of eight of the 10 brakes as a result of inadequate certification and test procedures (the brakes which failed were worn significantly). The takeoff warning was determined to have been a false alarm.

• In 1989, a USAir 737 crashed off the end of a runway at New York's La Guardia International Airport. The copilot was making the takeoff run when the aircraft began to drift to the left. Initially, attempts were made to steer the aircraft using the nose wheel tiller. As the ground run progressed, a loud "bang" was heard, and the captain elected to abort. The aircraft ran off the runway and into Bowery Bay. Two of the 57 passengers were killed, and 15 were injured. The crew escaped with minor injuries.

NTSB said the probable cause of the accident was the captain's failure to exercise his command authority in a timely manner to reject the takeoff or take sufficient control to continue the takeoff, which had been initiated with a mistrimmed rudder. The board said the crew's failure to detect the mistrimmed rudder prior to takeoff was a contributing factor.

Better to Go

These are only a few examples of RTO accidents. Worldwide, there have been at least 143 RTO accidents during the past 25 years.

Numerous studies have been conducted by NASA, NTSB, ALPA, McDonnell Douglas and Boeing. Common findings are that most accidents happen in situations where the RTO is initiated at or beyond V_1 with less than optimum runway conditions and less than optimum braking performance.

The researchers have found that almost half of the RTO accidents involved erroneous indications of systems failures, and they concluded that many of them would have had a much better outcome had the takeoff been continued instead of aborted.

The bottom line from the studies is that there is a need to reexamine V_1 procedures, and that for circumstances near or beyond V_1, continuing the takeoff is a much more viable decision.

GA Considerations

As mentioned earlier, very little attention has been paid to RTOs in general aviation operations. Among the reasons is the fact that most GA aircraft have the luxury of surplus performance in takeoff situations. Average ground run distances are less than 1,000 feet.

In many cases where a takeoff is aborted, the decision to abort happens early in the ground run, with plenty of runway in front.

In applying the concepts of RTO to general aviation, we must consider the following factors:

1. Pressure altitude and temperature. How does density altitude affect performance? (A pilot *may* have to abort a takeoff at a high-density-altitude airport, even if everything on his or her aircraft is working properly.)

2. Gross weight. Generally, the heavier the aircraft, the less performance we can expect. The takeoff roll will be longer.

3. Aircraft performance. Takeoff and climb performance, and braking capability must be taken into account.

4. Wind. Wind direction and speed can have a large effect not only on a normal takeoff, but on the RTO, as well.

5. Runway factors. Length, width, slope, condition, friction (dry, wet, icy), surrounding terrain and overrun availability should be considered.

On the Record

According to NTSB's records, general aviation aircraft are involved in about 15 to 20 takeoff-abort accidents per year. Though the aircraft are usually substantially damaged, in only a few of these cases are there fatalities or injuries.

Considering the average of 2,000 GA accidents per year, the statistics seem insignificant. However, the record also shows about 400 accidents each year have happened during the initial takeoff and climb phase. Many of these could have been prevented if the pilots had chosen to reject their takeoff attempts. These accidents have a relatively high fatality and injury rate.

Many of these accidents involved loss of power or loss of control resulting from circumstances which began to happen (and were detectable) before the aircraft left the ground.

In general aviation, therefore, we could surmise that the problem is the reverse of that in the air carrier world: Many GA accidents happen as a result of a decision to *continue* the takeoff, when a decision to abort would be more appropriate.

A good example was an accident that happened in the summer of 1988 at Grand Canyon Airport (elevation 6,600 feet). This airport routinely achieves density altitudes in excess of 10,000 feet in the summer. The aircraft, a Cessna 172 with four adults aboard, landed in the late afternoon for an en route fuel stop.

After taking on full fuel, the pilot attempted to take off, but the aircraft failed to climb. The pilot landed straight ahead on the 9,000-foot runway, taxied back to the active, did another run-up to clean the plugs and tried again. The second try had the same result as the first.

At this point, some judgment should have been applied. The aircraft obviously wasn't going to fly very well at that density altitude. The prudent choice would have been to wait a few hours for cooler temperatures.

The pilot elected to try again, however. He got the aircraft in the air, in ground effect, and there it stayed until it collided with the trees off the departure end. Three of the four occupants were killed; the fourth was severely injured.

Two good decisions to abort were made. Unfortunately, those two good decisions were followed by the third decision to keep flying. Whatever the pilot's reason for feeling that he had to get into the air, was it worth the price of the outcome?

The Urge to Go

There are several factors which could explain why a pilot might be inclined to continue a takeoff with questionable indications.

First, most of us have a strong motivation to get the aircraft into the air. Psychologically, we are unwilling to consider discontinuing a takeoff once we have started it, unless the indications that something is wrong are overwhelming.

Even though we may not be on a schedule or have to cope with pressure from an employer or customers to fly, our internal desire to make the flight can override our judgment process, and we press on.

I see this mind-set to fly in play often at an airport from which I frequently fly. The elevation is 5,000 feet, and the main runway is 7,000 feet long. On numerous occasions, I have watched pilots of retractable-gear aircraft pull the gear up almost as soon as they break ground, usually with about 6,000 feet of runway remaining.

What happens if the engine quits during the initial climb? If the gear is still down, no big deal—just land straight ahead. If the gear is up, there is, at least, going to be an expensive repair bill. About five years ago, a beautiful old Navion lost an engine in exactly that circumstance. The insurance company ended up "totaling" the aircraft.

Another factor is that modern aircraft, if properly maintained, seldom let us down. Mechanical failure has become relatively unusual, and pilots have become somewhat complacent.

We don't think about the possibility of a mechanical failure until there are indications that one is about to happen. Then we don't believe what we are seeing. For example, how many pilots have elected to make a takeoff, even though the run-up showed a greater-than-normal drop on one of the magnetos?

A third factor is that some pilots may be unacquainted with *all* of the characteristics of their aircraft.

Sometimes, this is a result of inadequate training or lack of experience, often due to the complacency mentioned above. It often is manifested in the failure to calculate weight and balance before takeoff, or to consider what effect an adverse loading condition would have on the ability to control the aircraft should something go wrong on takeoff.

Finally, some pilots fail to maintain adequate situational awareness during the takeoff roll. Their attention is focused on only part of their surroundings, and they may fail to notice critical indications that something isn't right.

Often, these pilots are saturated by the workload associated with takeoff and are actually withdrawn psychologically from what is happening to them. The result will be a delay in reacting to abnormal indications and an inability to adequately manage the results.

Conclusions

We should be ready, willing and able to abort a takeoff if there are any indications that something isn't right. We *must* be psychologically prepared to stop.

We should know our aircraft. What are its operational characteristics? How does weight and balance affect control and performance? What happens if something fails? Is it capable of partial performance?

We also should maintain situational awareness at all times. Know what is happening with the aircraft. Know what your options are in all situations.

Finally, we must avoid complacency. Accidents don't just happen to the other guy. Be prepared for the aircraft to let you down.

Let's change the environment a little. How do you deal with the situation when, for whatever reason, you can't turn back to the runway.

When There's No Way Back

Pilots occasionally find themselves in situations that make it impossible to return to the airport after departure. Though this predicament is most often associated with the infamous and ill-advised zero/zero takeoff, it can also occur when the weather is below minimums for the available approaches.

For example, taking off when there is a 500-foot ceiling and good visibility underneath the clouds is not a particularly difficult or dangerous task for an experienced and proficient instrument pilot flying a well-equipped and well-maintained aircraft.

But if the airport has only one published approach, and it has a minimum descent altitude (MDA) of 600 feet, that pilot had better plan to go somewhere else should the wheels begin falling off soon after takeoff.

Departures that allow no chance for return are not reserved for instrument weather conditions, either. There are many mountain flying situations in which wind and terrain can conspire to make a return to the airport impossible or, at least, impractical.

Also, when flying a light twin out of many high-altitude airports, the option of returning to the field following an engine failure is simply not available because of inadequate single-engine performance.

Keep in mind that all of these are difficult situations that can quickly become dangerous situations. Some pilots simply will not take off from an airport when conditions prohibit a return to the field shortly after takeoff. Some will not attempt to operate a twin-engine aircraft above its single-engine service ceiling.

Without a doubt, these conservative pilots have chosen the safest course of action. If the situation is difficult, they simply don't go. But many pilots consider flying as the business of managing an acceptable level of risk. Many are willing to accept certain risks, if they can be managed. This is the realm of any discussion about departures from airports that allow no return.

Recognizing the Risk

The first step, the one most often ignored, is to recognize when the situation exists.

Those who would dismiss themselves by saying, "I just don't fly under those conditions," are fooling themselves. They do it all the time; they just don't know it. Especially if they fly single-engine airplanes. There are certain emergencies that occur in single-engine airplanes which make a return to the airport impossible, regardless of the weather. Very few instrument approach procedures can be successfully completed in a glide.

Furthermore, if your only engine fails soon after lift-off, you had better not even think of returning to the airport. Your immediate destination is directly in front of you, give or take a few degrees of heading change.

Likewise, the published single-engine service ceilings for many light twins contain an element of fiction. If not fiction, at least optimism. At any given altitude, temperature and aircraft weight, you may be able to climb a hundred feet a minute or so when the aircraft is configured properly and the airspeed is at "blue line" (Vyse, the best single-engine rate of climb speed) or a few knots above. But in the same airplane, under the same conditions, you may not be able to climb at all if the airspeed gets one knot below blue line.

I recently encountered this situation when demonstrating a single-engine go-around in a UC-1 Twin Bee (a two-engine modification of the Seabee). With one engine feathered, the airplane was able to make two approaches and go-arounds. But on the third attempt, the airplane just couldn't accelerate to blue line in ground effect, and it was necessary to land in the water because we couldn't climb over the trees at the end of the lake.

So, many departures in twins have to be viewed from the standpoint of not returning to the airport. In high density altitude situations, the pilot has to have in mind a meadow or a road out beyond the departure end of the runway. In the event of an engine failure, he or she will then know where to go and will not attempt to make the airplane do something it cannot do.

Recognize the Situation

The key here is preparation. These factors have to be considered beforehand, and the plan of action has to be firmly implanted in the pilot's mind prior to takeoff.

The pilot must recognize a no-return situation when it exists and then formulate a strategy to cope with the emergency before it occurs.

Statistics tell us that many of the "emergencies" that occur when pilots cannot return to the airport are a direct result of poor preflight planning or inspection. A baggage door that pops open is only an annoyance under normal circumstances. But when the flight situation is more demanding, a neglected baggage compartment latch can prove fatal.

Hence, when no return to the airport is possible, preflight planning and pre-takeoff checklists become doubly important. Do a thorough preflight inspection of the aircraft, even if you have just flown it into the airport. Have the passengers stand away from the airplane or remain in the terminal while you do it. Don't allow any distractions. Use a checklist.

Likewise, before takeoff, go slowly through the pre-takeoff checklist. Don't allow the passengers to talk to you while you are doing it. Before rolling out on the runway, recheck the critical items, such as fuel tank selector positions, door security, boost pumps and mixtures. Whatever you do, don't hurry.

Preflight planning for a takeoff in instrument conditions is more difficult. Begin with the approaches for the airport you are departing from. What are the minimums? Analyze your proficiency and skill. It doesn't matter if the glide slope and localizer will bring you down to 200 feet and a half mile if you usually blow the approach at around 400 feet.

If the weather is below *your* minimums, you will have to go somewhere else should an emergency occur.

Always check the published departure procedures for the runways you might use. If there are none, do you know what to do to avoid hitting terrain while you are climbing to the minimum vectoring altitude in your area? If you're departing from an uncontrolled field, do you know how high you have to climb before ATC gets you in radio contact? In radar contact? You should know these things.

It also is important to ensure that the equipment in the airplane is working and the equipment on the ground is working. If the airport you are departing from has only an NDB approach and you haven't flown one in several years, you are in a no-return situation, especially if the NDB is located off the airport.

First Alternate

Once all of these factors have been considered, the next decision is where you are going to go if a problem occurs.

Ideally, what you are looking for is a wide, long runway a few miles away from the departure airport with an easy approach to low minimums. There should be a motel, lounge and car rental facilities near that runway. You will probably have to compromise on some of the items, but it is important that you select a "first alternate"—the airport where you plan to go in the event of problems on departure.

When you get your weather briefing, you will have to ask for the weather for your "first alternate," and be sure to ask for notams. This can easily be overlooked as the weather briefer loads you up with other information. So, write a note on your pad to get this information before you ring off.

Try to anticipate how you are going to transition from the departure procedure you will be flying to the approach procedure at your first alternate. Your radios will most likely be set to en route navaids. So, take a minute before takeoff to review what will be required in the event you have to divert.

In a sense, any time you have a communications failure after entering instrument conditions, you are in a no-return situation. Unless you filed your departure airport as your destination, ATC expects you to fly your flight plan, as filed, to your destination and follow the lost-communications procedures outlined in the FARs.

To return to the departure airport and shoot the approach without a clearance is dangerous and illegal, and will certainly result in the initiation of an FAA enforcement action.

Of course, as pilot-in-command, you are allowed to deviate from the rules to the degree necessary to meet the emergency. But you have to be able to justify your actions. Hence, a review of all the lost-communications procedures is in order. It is unreasonable to believe that you will be able to perform correctly when under stress if you can't remember the required procedures when seated in your easy chair.

Fly Your Plan

As when making a VFR departure, the pilot flying an IFR departure needs to have a clearly formulated and well-rehearsed plan to cope with emergencies soon after takeoff.

Much of what we need to know is contained in the departure clearance, but many of us have become desensitized to the important elements contained therein. Usually, as soon as we enter the clouds, we call up Departure Control, and the controller gives us vectors to where we are initially supposed to go.

Standard instrument departures (SIDs) can increase pilot apathy because these often very complicated procedures are usually overridden by Departure Control.

But what happens when Departure Control doesn't answer? Do you really know how to fly the departure procedure strictly under your own navigation? When was the last time you tried it?

Maintain Control

If something happens when the aircraft is just a few hundred feet in the air, whether IFR or VFR, the pilot has to suddenly maintain control, begin executing the emergency plan and deal with the problem.

Note the order in which I've presented these tasks, because success will depend not only upon the pilot doing the right things, but doing them in the right order.

Maintaining aircraft control is the most important and often the most difficult task. Although most pilots possess enough skill to keep the airplane under control in most emergencies, the emergency, itself, may scream for attention. Often, this distraction proves fatal.

In order to succeed, it is essential that the pilot keep his or her priorities in order. Always, *always*, aviate first, navigate second and do everything else last. If aircraft control requires all your attention, then that is where your attention must be. Let the engine burn or the baggage blow out the door, but don't lose control of the aircraft.

After a few seconds, aircraft control may become a little easier. Then you can move on to other things. The pilot who begins fiddling with the fuel selectors, carburetor heat, mixture control and boost pump immediately following an engine failure is doomed. What good does it do to have the engine roar to life just seconds before you strike the ground nose-first?

Once you get to the point that aircraft control doesn't require total concentration, you can begin doing those other things. It is important to have a well-rehearsed plan. If you already know where you are going to go and what you are going to do, there is at least a chance you will begin doing it.

On the other hand, this is not the time for creative thinking. It is not the time to begin reading and trying to understand the departure clearance. It is certainly not the time to begin leafing through the Jepp book in search of an airport at which you can land. Preparation and execution are what is going to get you out of difficulty.

We all know about the dangers of twins with only one operating engine, but what about total power loss on takeoff?

Often, the one and only choice is to land straight ahead. But not always: It is certainly preferable to set the airplane down on a runway (or the equivalent), and that's where good decision-making skills come into play.

Here's test pilot Bill Kelly again, with some words on how to make the right choice if you lose power at the worst possible moment.

Survival: Power Loss on Takeoff

Several weeks ago, I spent most of a day helping a friend fill out an accident report form. He had run his two-seat homebuilt off the end of a runway during an aborted takeoff. Only a few scrapes and bruises, but enough damage to require that the machine be disassembled and trucked 500 miles back to his workshop for repairs.

Although it was an incident, rather than an accident, "Ralph" still had to complete NTSB Form 6120.1. Besides getting some help in checking off the proper boxes on the form, Ralph was concerned about how he had handled the emergency situation and wanted to talk it over.

I had worked with him on the initial test flights of his homebuilt and was impressed with his flying ability, thoroughness and judgment. So, before tackling the NTSB form, we talked for a long time.

It seems that Ralph was returning with his wife from his first real trip in the airplane. They had stopped for fuel at an airport in the hill country of Tennessee. It has one runway, 5,000- by 75-feet of pavement oriented north-south.

Winds were light and variable, so Ralph followed the rest of the traffic in departing on Runway 18, which has a slight uphill gradient for the first 3,000 feet and a downhill gradient for the last 1,000-foot portion.

Engine run-up was normal, but Ralph cannot recall static rpm with full throttle when he started the takeoff roll. The homebuilt had a fixed-pitch "cruise" prop—with maybe a little too much pitch, and we had found takeoff and climb power from the Lycoming O-320 to be somewhat low. During the flight tests, we were getting only about 2,200 rpm static, but the prop seemed OK for high-speed cruise, where rpm nearly touched the redline 2,700 rpm at full throttle and low altitude.

Decision Time
Ralph said the takeoff run and liftoff seemed normal, even with the uphill gradient, but the initial climb was sluggish. The airspeed was greater than Vy on liftoff but dropped by 10 mph before the homebuilt was 20 feet off the ground.

Ralph lowered the nose just a tad to hold speed, but the climb rate still seemed too low. The approaching terrain wasn't inviting, and there seemed to be enough runway remaining on which to land and stop. It was decision time.

Ralph decided to abort. He landed, put on the binders—and found that he was already over the crest of the slight rise onto what appeared to be a steeply downward sloping runway. Off went the mixture, fuel valve, mags and electrical system.

Picking a Spot
The runway has no overrun, and the terrain off the departure end drops very steeply into a rough and wooded area. But Ralph saw that just a little to the right, the terrain appeared smoother and had a shallower slope.

He went for it, and the airplane rolled off the pavement onto the grass at about 20 mph. Unfortunately, a little rain gully cuts through the grass. The nose wheel broke free when it hit the gully, and the prop tip splintered. But the airplane remained upright; there were no fuel leaks, and no fire. Ralph and his wife walked away with only a few scrapes and bruises.

Naturally, Ralph came to have some second thoughts about his decision to abort: *Maybe it was climbing OK. Maybe, if I had just steadied on Vy, we would have cleared those trees. Maybe that rolling terrain had me confused and I just didn't set the right pitch attitude after liftoff. Maybe....*

Maybe Not

I'm happy that Ralph decided to abort. I would be even happier had he checked his engine static rpm and compared it to earlier engine performance (see the "ground power check" discussion on page 4 of the Aug. 15 issue).

But, overall, I think that Ralph made the proper decision. It's much better to roll into a low-speed minor crunch off the far end of the runway than to press ahead when things don't seem right and fly into a real killer crash.

It turns out that Ralph really *did* have an engine problem. Investigators found the carburetor slightly loose on its mounting; one hold-down nut was missing, and the other three were loose. Imagine what might have happened if Ralph had tried to continue flying. It's a good guess that an over-lean mixture from the loose carb eroded power and climb performance. If he had continued, power might have been lost completely.

Sure, Ralph's pride-and-joy was damaged. But, at least he's alive and well, and able to repair the homebuilt. When we came to the section of the NTSB form that asks for recommendations on how the accident could have been prevented, Ralph answered, "I should have decided sooner to abort."

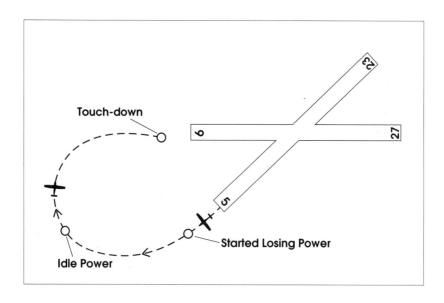

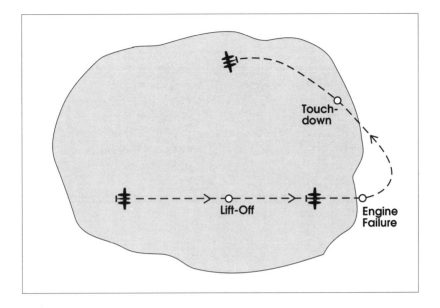

Fast Action

Ralph recognized his problem and took the proper action relatively early in the takeoff sequence. Several years ago, another pilot, "Don," had a similar experience—but his problem occurred a little later, as his Cherokee was passing over the end of the runway and climbing through 300 feet.

Before taking off on Runway 23, Don had checked carefully for carburetor ice but saw no telltale indications. It was a cloudy day, with no rain, and the temperature was in the 70s. Engine power appeared steady during the ground run and initial climb, but then the rpm started dropping rapidly.

Don lowered the nose and bent the Cherokee into an immediate right turn, hoping to return to Runway 9, which intersects 23 (see the accompanying illustration). He also applied carburetor heat and even had time to switch fuel tanks. But power kept falling. Before the airplane had completed even half of the needed 225-degree turn, the power output had dropped almost to idle.

Don used to fly crop-dusters and is familiar with the danger of low-altitude turns. He avoided steep banks and kept his airspeed up. Though he was able to line up for Runway 9, the Cherokee was too low to make it to the concrete. So, he landed in a clear, grassy area 1,000 feet short of the runway. Unfortunately, the area is very rough, and the airplane was substantially damaged (wrinkled wings).

No Man's Land

The investigation of Don's accident wasn't as thorough as it should have been. The bent prop was replaced, and the engine appeared to run fine during a short test on the ground. Carb ice was deemed the culprit, but I sure wish the investigation had included a flow check of the Cherokee's fuel system and a bench check of the carburetor.

But, what really matters here is that the pilot reacted well to the situation. When the problem became apparent, Don was in a no man's land where *maybe* he could return to the airport *if* the engine continued putting out some power. But the engine didn't cooperate, and the pilot landed the Cherokee in fairly good terrain.

Don says the only reason he turned back toward the airport was that the engine initially was still producing some power. He said that if all power had been lost, he would have landed straight ahead, under control—albeit in fairly rough terrain. That's good thinking.

Check It Out

Another important point is that Don knew the terrain around the airport. He knew where the populated areas were. He knew where the trees were. He knew that the approach area to Runway 9 was clear and flat—he just didn't realize it was so rough. He knew the Cherokee's engine-out glide speed, and he knew he could not bank steeply at that speed.

Don's decision-making was based on years of local experience. Ralph had only seconds to plan his arrival, but he still picked the best possible spot in which to land his airplane.

How often, when you are entering the traffic pattern at an unfamiliar airport, do you observe the areas nearby? Do you check for reasonable "crash-landing" sites near the ends of each of the runways? When's the last time you checked out the area surrounding your local airport? In just the past year, a new housing development, a big industrial park and a deep phosphate quarry have sprouted around my local field, eliminating some good emergency landing areas. But there are still a few clear areas left between the developments.

Walk Away

Another thought: *Don't concern yourself with damage to the airplane.* Your concern should be surviving the forced landing with minimum injury to yourself, your passengers and those innocent bystanders on the ground. Statistics show that the airplane probably *will* be damaged. If you try too hard to "save" the airplane—by trying to turn back to the airport, for instance—people may be injured or killed.

Let the insurance company worry about damage; that's why you pay those tremendous hull premiums. You should worry instead about walking away from the wreckage and about expensive lawsuits that could be brought by injured people, especially your passengers.

Don't try a desperate turn back to the airport. Don't try forcing the airplane onto a curving, narrow dirt road flanked with ditches, when there is a reasonably level field available. The reports I read show a large percentage of landings on narrow roads end up with a wing tip catching on a tree or road sign, or a high-speed dive into a ditch. Maybe a controlled touchdown in the pasture—even with its fences, gullies and cattle—would be less damaging and injurious.

Quick Turn

We'll go into more detail on the infamous turn back to the airport later in this report. But first, let's look at one more example of how a pilot coped with a power loss on takeoff.

The pilot, "Charles," had been instructing in float-equipped J-3 Cubs for quite a while and knew that floatplane cold. He knew, for instance, that you have to shove the nose down hard, almost to zero G, if the engine quits on initial climb, because drag from the floats kills airspeed quickly. He also knew that this floatplane is only good for about 180 degrees of turn from an altitude of 500 feet at glide speed with a dead

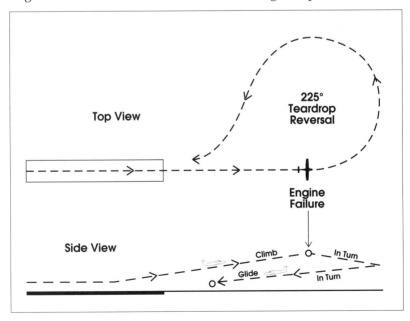

or idling engine. He was also familiar with the local training lakes and surrounding terrain.

So, when power was lost just as he was passing 300 feet over the upwind end of a big, round lake on takeoff, Charles was able to do a quick 120-degree turn back to a water landing. He landed right off the upwind shoreline. (If it had been a wheel-equipped Cub on a hard-surface runway, he would *not* have been successful in trying for a downwind landing on the runway.)

Don't Look Back

Now we get to the nitty-gritty: When *can* you try that big turn back to the runway after losing the engine on takeoff?

In my opinion, the best advice in most cases is: *Don't turn back.* Don't count on getting back to the runway if you lose power during a straight-out departure. If you're left with some power, as Don was, maybe it's worth the try. But if the engine fails completely after you have already passed the far end of the runway, the chances are not very good for making a successful reversal to land downwind on the same runway. (There are exceptions, of course. I'm talking about the typical 3,000- to 4,000-foot GA runway. At a big airport, you might have enough altitude by the time you pass the departure end of a 10,000-foot runway to return safely.)

First consideration: It's not just a simple 180-degree turn. It's going to be a teardrop of about 225 degrees, followed by another 45-degree turn to line up with the pavement. That's a total of 270 degrees of turn. Throw in some straight flight to connect the teardrop with the final approach, and you have the equivalent of a 360-degree power-off turn.

And you'll be losing altitude fast. In straight-and-level flight, your glide ratio would be about 6:1 in a draggy fixed-gear airplane or, maybe, as much as 10:1 in a clean retractable with the gear up. But even that meager glide performance would suffer while maneuvering through a series of turns.

In a shallow, 15-degree banked turn (close to standard rate at glide speed in most GA airplanes), induced drag is seven percent higher than with wings level. Steepen the bank to 30 degrees, and induced drag at the same indicated airspeed will increase by 33 percent. At 45 degrees, count on doubling that wing drag. Don't even dream of banking 60 degrees; even if you don't stall and spin, descent rate will be astronomical to counter that 300 percent increase in induced drag.

What Speed?

Remember that G load and stall speeds are functions of bank angle. A turn with 45 degrees of bank requires 1.4 G, and stall speed is increased almost 20 percent. With 60 degrees of bank, you need 2 G, and stall speed is increased 40 percent. You just *cannot* bend an airplane around in steep turns at the published "best glide" airspeed.

My old Cessna 182 manual posts 80 mph IAS as the wings-level maximum glide speed. That's *less* than the 91 mph CAS listed as stall speed in a 60-degree bank. My Piper Lance manual is a little newer and provides IAS values for everything. It says Vs_1 (clean stall speed) varies from about 56 knots with wings level to almost 80 knots with a 60-degree bank. Best glide speed is quoted as 92 knots (for wings-level, of course). Therefore, a safe glide speed in a 60-degree banked turn would be roughly in the vicinity of 120 to 130 knots!

The point of this exercise on airspeeds, G load and stall speeds is to emphasize that the published best-glide airspeed holds only for straight-and-level flight. You'd have to increase that value by 20 percent for a turn with 45 degrees of bank, 40 percent for 60 degrees.

Tight Turns

Don't count on using steep turns to get you back to the airport following an engine failure on takeoff. A tight turn will reduce the distance traveled over the ground, but it will consume altitude. It also could consume everybody aboard if you lose control, stall and spin.

Remember those ground reference maneuvers your CFI had you practice during your primary training? Did you have a little trouble with airspeed and pitch control during those pylon turns and S-turns across the road in high winds? We all did. Do you *really* want to play a similar game with the airplane even closer to the ground, in a steep descent with a dead engine?

So, keep those gliding turns to the maximum bank angles you would use in a normal traffic pattern (hopefully in the vicinity of 15-20 degrees and never more than 30 degrees). With 30 degrees of bank, stall speed is increased only about seven percent, so you should still have sufficient margin at the published best-glide speed—maybe add five knots just to be safe.

Turn Tests

I tried a few turn-arounds in a Cessna 152 at 1,000-2,500 feet AGL just for my own edification. Results of the flight tests are detailed in the accompanying article; but, to sum up, I found I could "teardrop" the little bird back to a downwind heading, using 30 degrees of bank for the turns, with a loss of between 600 and 700 feet of altitude.

But that was with the engine idling. With a dead engine and a windmilling propeller, drag would have been a little higher and more altitude would have been lost. And I was only trying to turn to the final approach heading. Had it been the real thing, I would still have had to be concerned with how far away the runway was when I rolled out on that heading. If I ended up too short (as Don did), a downwind touchdown short of the paved surface would have resulted. Too long, and I'd be faced (like Ralph in his homebuilt) with a possible overshoot on a short runway.

If you want to get a better handle on what it takes to maneuver your own airplane through the teardrop turn-back, I'd suggest you try it at a safe altitude. Limit bank to 30 degrees, maximum, for all turns. Simulate the power failure while climbing at Vy (best rate-of-climb airspeed) and get a feeling for the amount of push-over needed to transition quickly to the best glide speed. Don't start turning any slower than that.

Use a straight road to simulate the runway. Climb out directly over and parallel to the road, and plan the teardrop to return back over the road. Record your altitude loss and average rate of descent.

My guess is that you will learn enough from a few of these maneuvers to decide against ever attempting a low-altitude turn-around.

Pick Your Spot

A better bet if your engine ever quits during that first minute or two after liftoff is to look no more than 60 degrees to the right and left, and pick a place to land somewhere within that 120-degree arc.

Plan on being on a wings-level final to your touchdown point no lower than 200 feet AGL. No low-altitude steep turns. Use that last 200 feet to get ready for a *well-controlled* touchdown at the lowest possible safe airspeed. Use some flaps if you can, just to lower touchdown speed, but don't automatically drop full flaps unless you are ready to handle the rapid deceleration and increased descent rate.

If you're flying a retractable-gear airplane, you'll have to decide whether or not to extend the landing gear. Personally, I'll give up that nebulous shock-absorbing benefit of extended gear if the terrain appears too soft for the gear to support the airplane. I would prefer a hard belly landing to a turn-over. A lot of our GA airplanes are hard enough to exit when right-side-up; some cannot be evacuated when upside-down due to jammed doors, sliding canopies or disoriented passengers.

Summary

As mentioned earlier, figure that an engine failure after takeoff is probably going to wreck the airplane. So be it. That's the insurance carrier's worry. Yours is to preserve lives, and that means concentrating on making the best touchdown of your whole flying career—even if it's into stumps, boulders or a mixed herd of Holsteins and Guernseys.

Make gentle heading corrections while you still have a little altitude, to miss the old oak tree or that big Brahma bull. Your work on the yoke and rudder pedals should be just like those last-minute corrections you make to stay on runway centerline during a normal landing.

Know your power-off emergency landing checklist *cold* and have it completed before touchdown. Make sure, for instance, that you shut off the fuel flow and electrical power, and, on some airplanes, unlatch the door.

Finally, there's another very important consideration—a critical item that should be attended to even before you start the engine back on the ramp: the passenger briefing. Your passengers should be briefed on such things as how to open the cabin door and the emergency exits, and how to tighten their restraint straps. Give your passengers a chance, just in case you are incapacitated in the crash landing.

En Route

I *n the middle of a flight things are less time-critical than at takeoff or landing, but no less important, particularly for an IFR pilot.*

We've covered many of the decisions a pilot is called on to make en route in previous volumes. We'll revisit some of them here, and introduce a few new ideas, as well.

First we'll talk in general about some factors that affect your ability to deal with crises in the air. Here we have Brian Jacobson, a 10,000-hour corporate pilot.

Staying Ahead of the Airplane

After 15 minutes of flying the Turbo Commander, I knew I needed practice. It had been almost 15 years since I had flown a high-performance airplane without a second pilot, and it showed. It took a few approaches before I felt comfortable again.

The experience reminded me that single-pilot IFR requires a certain rhythm. A pilot develops it with experience and discipline. It can be lost if not practiced regularly, as I proved to myself after flying with a second-in-command for so long.

As you gain experience and become comfortable with flying on the gauges, a pattern begins to develop by which the flying workload is managed. It manifests itself over time in the way you do everything in the cockpit.

The pattern generally builds from the way you use your written or mental checklists. The type of airplane and the equipment with which he or she has to work will decide how a pilot develops strategies for workload management.

Often, however, the pattern must be modified, and the pilot must resort to different tactics to complete a flight safely. For example, many pilots rely on autopilots to relieve much of the pressure associated with instrument and high-density terminal operations.

An autopilot is a great tool; but Murphy's Law states that if it breaks, it probably will do so on the worst IFR day of the year. Therefore, pilots should always be ready, willing and able to hand-fly the airplane while attending to all the other tasks of instrument flying.

Over-reliance on an autopilot can lead to trouble. For example, I knew a pilot whose company insisted that he acquire an instrument rating to keep his job flying their Beech Baron. He had been flying VFR for 20 years and didn't really want to learn new tricks. He got the rating but didn't like flying in the soup. He canceled most flights that required it. When he did fly in IMC, he relied on the autopilot.

Once, I was in the right seat of the Baron on a trip that required several instrument approaches. He turned on the autopilot right after each takeoff and didn't turn it off until the runway was in sight. Fortunately, the weather was at or near VFR minimums; had the autopilot failed, he probably would have broken out in time to make a visual approach and landing—so long as events didn't get too far out of hand while he was in the clouds.

Saturation Point

The faster the aircraft, the faster the pilot has to process information from the gauges and/or from outside the cockpit. Workload saturation results when a pilot is unable to keep up with everything that is happening.

As things continue to pile up, the pilot's performance deteriorates. He starts to fixate, attempting to correct one problem at a time.

Workload saturation also can arise from inexperience. For instance, a student instrument pilot will become saturated quickly if his instructor administers too many tasks too early. The CFII's job is to help the student develop his skills so, as the training progresses, he can assume more of the workload. Before his training is complete, the student will cultivate a system of doing all required tasks in a repetitive and orderly manner that he follows from takeoff to landing.

An instrument pilot who flies alone and without an autopilot might want to consider taking along a simple flight log that lists, for the airways to be used, each navaid identifier and frequency, plus the inbound and outbound radials. This reduces the need to search charts for the same information and frees up more time for monitoring the instruments.

The landing phase is the toughest, especially for new or infrequent instrument pilots. Sometimes, it is easier for the pilot to complete the approach by himself, without vectors from ATC. That way, he is always aware of his position and can follow the procedure on the approach plate during each step. While on vectors, it is easy to lose positional awareness, especially if the controller is busy and issues several course changes.

A pilot is most likely to overlook checklist items if he is not completing his tasks quickly enough.

Some pilots use written checklists for everything, while others develop mental checklists for certain phases of flight. Using a written checklist is no guarantee a pilot will complete each item.

The classic example is the airline crew which neglected to turn on the pitot heat while completing a written before-takeoff checklist. The aircraft crashed out of control when the instruments gave false readings and the crew did not realize what the problem was.

A pilot who is smooth and efficient will have the time to use written checklists, if he so desires. There are mnemonics ("GUMP," for instance) which can be just as effective. But, no matter which method you use, keep in mind that as workload increases and situations demand a change from routine, it is very easy to overlook a critical item—whether it is on a checklist, approach plate or the instrument panel.

Pilots who do not fly often may also be subject to workload saturation. I have several friends who maintain their instrument currency by going out every six months and doing their six hours and six approaches over a one- or two-day period with a safety pilot in the right seat.

While perfectly legal, it would not be prudent for one of these pilots to file and fly actual instruments late in the currency period unless weather conditions were such that any approaches flown would be for practice. Taking along another pilot could help to reduce the workload, but there must be a firm understanding before launching of the duties of each pilot.

Much can be done before beginning a flight to avoid surprises in a high-density area. Investigate routings that may be issued to you and file one you are likely to get. "Preferred routes" are listed in the *Airport/Facility Directory*. A call to the FSS or local approach control facility also can help you decide what routing to expect. Most high-density areas use certain fixes or "gates" for arrivals and departures. You will find them depicted on SIDS, STARS and local area charts.

Get the Picture

When you receive your clearance, give yourself enough time to become familiar with what ATC expects you to do.

Cranking up and taking off without a good picture in your mind of what the clearance is and where it is going to take you can get you into trouble. Be especially wary if your clearance is different from the routing you filed.

Flying an assigned routing will be a lot easier if you develop a picture of it in your mind. When you look down at your chart, flight log or approach plate, what you see will already be familiar. This will reduce the time your eyes are away from the instruments.

Trying to find an airway while keeping the airplane on course and climbing to a cruise altitude could be difficult. Add calls from the controller with a course or altitude change, and you probably will wish you were flying a simulator from which you could get up and walk away.

Consider what would happen if you lost communications while attempting to do all of this. Or your nav radios. Or the autopilot. Frustrations resulting from the inability to cope with problems can build quickly and result in disorientation and loss of control.

How do you develop a pattern or rhythm in your everyday flying? It's simple. Strive to do things the same way every time you fly. Even when flying VFR, conduct the preflight, start-up, before-takeoff checklist and departure the same way every time.

When IFR in IMC, keep up a good instrument scan. Each third or fourth time around the panel, check the engine instruments, ammeter and suction gauge. When flying IFR in VFR conditions, make sure you include looking out the window in your scan.

Efficiency is paramount in keeping your workload manageable. Develop your instrument scan to absorb the most information in the shortest amount of time. If it seems you are having trouble with your scan or find yourself not completing your tasks quickly enough, get a flight instructor or safety pilot to ride with you and relieve you of some of the chores, such as talking to ATC or handling the navigation, while you concentrate on improving your basic instrument flying.

Beating Saturation

As your technique improves, you will find yourself able to take on the additional workload without becoming saturated. As you acquire experience, you will find yourself more confident in your ability to fly and complete your tasks smoothly and efficiently.

Then, when unusual circumstances demand a change in routine, it will be far easier for you to adapt.

It took many years for the aviation community to realize the extent to which "human factors" contribute to accidents. The airlines and some corporate flight departments are striving to make use of cockpit resources management (CRM) to enhance the working relationships among crew members. Some principles of CRM can apply to the single pilot. If you consider yourself a manager trying to fulfill some difficult tasks to achieve a stated goal—that of getting an aircraft safely from point A to point B—you can reason that certain things must take priority over others.

Every pilot knows that no matter what occurs, you must always *fly the airplane*, first. This is task number one, taking precedence over all others.

However, pilots often let other tasks take precedence over aircraft control. For instance, many pilots allow the task of calling their position on each leg of the traffic pattern to interrupt their concentration on the approach. As a result, their approaches are not stable and result in poor landings. While every attempt should be made to let others know where you are in the pattern, flying the aircraft should be given top priority.

Fly the airplane, first. Then, assign priorities to other requirements and actions. (Making the call on downwind can wait until the aircraft is properly configured and at the right airspeed and altitude, for instance.) Decide what actions take precedence over others.

By the time you complete a certain phase of flight, if something has not been attended to, it should be of such low priority that it won't really matter.

Dangers of Distraction

Distraction often causes pilots to abandon the number one priority of flying the aircraft.

For example, many accidents have occurred after pilots became preoccupied with closing cabin doors that had popped open on takeoff. The aircraft could have been flown, but the pilots let their concentration be absorbed by the noise and buffeting of the open doors. There are many other examples of distractions which lured pilots from the primary task of flying their aircraft.

There are many pilots who consider the "management" approach wrong for general aviation. They claim it takes the fun out of flying because we are no longer "pilots" in the traditional sense. While there is some truth to that, it does not change the fact that operating in today's environment demands this kind of attention, especially from pilots who fly alone.

There are always many different approaches to the same problem. Each of us develops our own techniques for dealing with cockpit workload. If, after the airplane is safely in its hangar or tie-down, you are satisfied that you completed all the important tasks, then your approach to the problem is probably a safe one.

Each of us must ensure that when we step into the cockpit, we remain the master of the ship, even if the workload does exceed our expectations.

A good method of beating increasing cockpit stress is to make contingency plans.

It's vital, as we saw in the first section, to make these plans ahead of time, so that you're not forced into a situation of making things up as you go along.

Beating the Breaking Point

With good training and practice, most of us can safely make our way about the airways under instrument flight rules. When all is going according to plan, there is plenty of time to accomplish all the tasks required to safely fly in the clouds. On a familiar route with the autopilot keeping us on course and the DME ticking off the miles, it is even possible to relax a little.

But when unforecast severe weather catches us off guard, when equipment failure increases cockpit workload, or when complicated clearances or routings are thrown at us out of the blue, we can become overloaded to the breaking point.

To avoid this potential for disaster, an instrument pilot must develop a set of contingency plans to fall back on when the workload becomes critical. Having to fly to a strange airport and execute a difficult approach under high-stress conditions is tough enough. But having to decide *which* airport to turn to and which approach to shoot can be overwhelming.

An examination of single-pilot IFR accidents will show that when a pilot is under considerable stress, his or her ability to find creative solutions to difficult problems is severely restricted. The only way we can protect ourselves from being overwhelmed by the circumstances is to do our creative thinking during the initial planning stages of the flight, so that when the chips are down, we can react without a lot of mental gymnastics.

The route is usually the first thing we consider when planning an IFR flight. If the route you file or the route you are likely to be assigned leads you over high terrain, take just a moment to compare the IFR chart with a VFR chart and mark where the airways cross the highest points of terrain. Measure the distances to these points from navaids and note them on the chart.

These "high points" are points-of-no-return in the event that you cannot maintain altitude on the airway. If the high point is in front of you when the engine starts to lose power, you know your best bet is to turn around. If the high point is behind you when you start picking up a horrendous load of ice, you know the lower terrain is in front of you and your best bet is to hold heading.

What If?

Also, when considering the route, take a look at the big picture and ask yourself this question: "If I were to lose all electrical capability—all navigation and communication capability—where would I want to go to make a letdown?"

The odds of this happening are remote. But going through the exercise will implant in your mind the direction and nature of the most hospitable terrain. You will pre-program yourself to point the airplane in that direction during a crisis.

Finally, assess the route you have chosen for overall safety. Often, it is wise to choose a less direct route if that route will keep you out of harm's way. You may not be assigned the longer route, but it certainly doesn't hurt to ask. A comment like "Routing selected for aircraft performance" in the remarks box on a flight plan can sometimes help.

Remember, the route you are assigned often is not the route you want, but the route ATC wants you on in the event you experience communications failure. Once airborne, with communications and competence established in the mind of the controller, you can usually get the routing you wanted in the first place.

The next important step is to compare your route to the weather conditions. If your flight parallels a mountain range, and if there are substantial winds aloft, will you be flying on the upwind side of the mountains or the downwind side?

If there is a front involved in the weather picture, will you be flying parallel to it, or can you choose a route that will get you behind the front quickly? If you are planning to cross the front, will you do so over high terrain, or can you alter your route to cross the front in a more favorable area?

Of course, this type of flight planning is not specific to single-pilot operations. It's a good practice regardless of crew size.

Selecting Alternates

Once the route is decided upon, the high points marked and the escape routes planned, it's time to consider alternate airports.

Notice the use of the plural. Although there is only one blank for the alternate airport on the flight plan form, the pilot should have several alternates in mind.

The airport listed in the box on the flight plan is the alternate airport to which you are going to proceed in the event that you lose communications capability and cannot land at your destination.

I have several personal requirements for this airport. First, it should have long runways and an ILS approach. It should have rental cars available, and it should have a restaurant on the field...with a lounge.

If there is enough fuel aboard the airplane, I file my home base as an alternate. That's where my car is. That's where the radio shop is. And I know the approach like the back of my hand. Why not come home if you've got the gas?

Usually, when we need an alternate airport, the radios are working fine and during the missed approach we simply tell the controller where we want to go—that is, if we know where we want to go. Hence, we need a second alternate—the one we want to go to if everything but the weather is working right.

Though the final choice will probably be the result of a discussion with the controller, it is important that you consider several options prior to the flight.

Obviously, the alternates you consider should provide a better chance of a successful approach than the original destination. If the destination is socked in because of ground fog, don't even consider an alternate that is down in the river bed. If your destination only has a VOR approach, don't pick a nearby alternate unless the approach offers substantially lower minimums. For preflight planning purposes, don't consider an alternate which uses the same approach facility, because if that facility is suddenly out of service, you won't be able to make an approach there, either.

Try to anticipate why you might have to miss the approach at your destination and pick alternates that won't be affected by the same circumstances.

The third, fourth and fifth alternates are airports along the route to which you might want to divert if the wheels begin falling off during cruise. Take a look at the chart and select several airports that offer safe harbors in the event of an emergency. Try to find airports with ILS approaches, because all ILS approaches are essentially the same. Put a paper clip on each of these charts so that if you have to head for one, you don't spend a lot of time leafing through the book in moderate to severe turbulence.

Gloom and Doom

Of course, many of the decisions you will make regarding route and alternates will be made after consideration of the weather.

Changes in the weather-reporting system, as well as changes in the way the reports are delivered to the consumer have changed the ways pilots gather data.

Today, the "big picture" is available to almost anyone with cable television. Programs such as *A.M. Weather* and the continuous *Weather Channel* make graphic depictions of the weather map available in the comfort of your living room. Though the information displayed on the screen comes from the National Weather Service and is quite accurate, the conclusions drawn by the commentators are not always valid forecasts. Start out with a synopsis of the weather from the television and then press on to a complete weather briefing from the FAA.

Today, aviation weather is available to home computer users via a modem and DUAT or one of the commercial services. But, most of us still rely on a telephone briefing to gather flight-planning information. Because of the nature of our litigious society, weather briefings seem to be structured more around tort law than natural laws. In order to get the facts you need, it is necessary to separate the meteorological wheat from the legal and bureaucratic chaff.

Let me provide an analogy to help you to better understand where FAA weather briefers are coming from these days. Imagine that you called the downtown theater to find out about the movies showing and received this information: "Tonight we are showing `Dances With Wolves.' Patrons are urged to park under bright lights and not to leave valuables in their automobiles. The city has declared the area around the theater a high-crime zone, and women as well as men unfamiliar with martial arts are encouraged to run from their cars to the theater. Be advised that last week, a couple was assaulted within a block of the theater."

Would you want to go to that movie?

I sure wouldn't. Yet, I've been to hundreds of movies in downtown areas around the country and have never been molested. Most theaters in metropolitan areas could issue the same warnings. They simply don't. Because if they did, no one would ever go to the movies.

On the other hand, the FAA doesn't care if you ever go flying. They would much rather make absolutely sure that you know all the risks than to have you blast off uninformed. Hence, the first part of any FAA weather briefing is a litany of "flight precautions" and other gloom-and-doom information designed and worded for the specific purpose of giving you plenty of reasons to cancel your flight. If you don't really want to go flying, the weather briefing will give you good justification for staying by the fire. If, on the other hand, you want to go, you have to take a more critical look at the information presented.

Analyzing the Weather

First of all, remember that forecasts are merely predictions. Based on the data available, they are educated guesses that there might be a good chance of severe weather—turbulence, icing, thunderstorms or whatever.

But just because there is a good chance of these events, that doesn't mean that they will actually occur. Even if they do occur, they may not affect the route you have selected.

This is where pilot reports are invaluable. If there is a forecast of moderate to severe turbulence along your route, and if there is a fresh pilot report by a Cessna 172 pilot who made the flight with only occasional moderate turbulence, you can probably duplicate his route with similar results. On the other hand, if the pilot of a King Air reports severe turbulence at the altitudes you would fly, you'd better think about driving.

A forecast of embedded thunderstorms should catch the attention of any pilot considering single-pilot IFR. Like the old saying goes, with thunderstorms, there's some good news and some bad news. The bad news is that some thunderstorms contain sufficient energy to chew up an airplane and spit it out. The good news is that thunderstorms can be seen by radar.

So, after the weather man gives you the death-and-destruction forecast, ask him to take a look at the radar summary chart. He or she can tell you where the thunderstorms are and in what direction they are moving. It's not uncommon to find out—only after asking—that the closest thunderstorm is 200 miles from your route.

The interpretation of airborne weather radar by a single pilot is an iffy proposition. For most operations, it takes one person to keep the airplane right-side-up while the other pilot tries to find a way through the hot spots. A Stormscope is a little easier to interpret, but picking your way through the cells is about as difficult as any single-pilot operation will ever get. If you're that good, then go for it. But you had better be good.

To get the most out of a weather briefing for single-pilot IFR, it is necessary to learn how to read between the lines. Once you have the forecast, compare it to the actual weather. When a cold front is scheduled to arrive soon, get the sequence reports from several stations north of the area to see how things are progressing. If the wind shifts more than 90 degrees at your location, the front has just passed, whether the forecasters know it or not.

Learn to assess all the data you get from the weather forecasters critically and always compare actual weather with the forecast.

Ready for Anything

Once you have chosen your route and alternates in light of the prevailing weather conditions, it's time to develop a series of contingency plans to meet most emergencies.

Move your finger along the chart and ask yourself what you would do if you had an icing encounter, electrical failure, nav radio failure, comm radio failure, vacuum system failure or powerplant failure.

Take just five minutes to anticipate the most common situations and you will pre-load your brain for the emergency. Then, when it arrives, you will have already thought about what you are going to do and where you are going to go.

If you encounter icing, for instance, are you going to try to climb on top, or are you going to head for warmer air over lower terrain? If you have a total electrical system failure, what procedures are you going to follow and where can you go to get back to VFR and a safe landing? If the vacuum system checks out, which airports along the way can provide a no-gyro approach? Better yet, where can you go to land VFR? And if the engine expires, which heading offers the best chances for a successful emergency landing?

All of these questions, if asked and answered prior to takeoff, reduce the pressure on a pilot dramatically and increase the chances of making the correct decisions later on.

In this successful society, we are encouraged to think optimistically. Success is the frequent product of the power of positive thinking. But when it comes to single-pilot IFR, a certain amount of negative thinking is important. The person who hopes for the best, who believes that his flight will go without difficulties, who applies the power of positive thinking to his flight planning, is setting himself up for disaster.

If you fly long enough, there will come a time when you are simply overwhelmed with the demands of instrument flying. When that time comes, if you have a contingency plan to fall back on, if you have spent some time considering the possibilities prior to the flight, you will have a pre-planned way out.

Good decisions require the pilot to have all the pertinent information available at a moment's notice. Flying along in the crud is no time to be guessing a critical airspeed or power setting.

While having this information at your fingertips is not likely to make or break a flight, it will free you up to concentrate on the important part.

Many pilots cook up their own crib sheets, containing the information they find useful. We're not talking about checklists, here, but rather the information you'd normally dig into the flight manual for. Here's Lear pilot and editor Mark Lacagnina with his version of the cheat sheet.

Memory Aids

Good, it's vectors to final for the ILS. *That certainly will help,* the pilot sighs, *but this approach isn't necessarily going to be a piece of cake.* The weather is hovering at minimums and the surface winds are a maelstrom. Staccato bursts of rain on the airframe and ceaseless chatter on the frequency conspire to create a terrific din in the cabin, and the passengers become uneasy as the aircraft descends in increasingly rough air.

Now the jolts are beginning to throw everyone against their restraints. *Glad I had them secure their belts before we started down,* the pilot muses. He instinctively reaches for the throttle when one particularly nasty bump takes his breath away. As he glances at the airspeed indicator, which is twitching like a maniac's eyelid, he realizes that he hasn't the foggiest idea of how he should set the power controls to achieve maneuvering speed during the descent. *I'll just back off a few inches. That should do it.*

His attention is caught by the ammeter. *That's not right. That's way too high, isn't it?* As he puzzles over this new problem, everything seems to happen at once. The altimeter needle swings rapidly by the assigned altitude, and somewhere amid the babble on the radio was the aircraft's call sign. The pilot detects a hard edge to the controller's voice as he is told again that he's two miles from the localizer and to report the marker.

The cockpit has become very warm, and the pilot finds it difficult to keep a firm grasp on the yoke. Ignoring the discomfort, he commends himself for the job he's doing in manhandling the bucking, twisting aircraft to keep the altimeter and localizer needles in some semblance of proper order. But the good feeling is short-lived when the hooting of the marker beacon awakens him to the fact that airspeed is still way too high—above the gear-extension limit, in fact—and that the glide slope needle is heading toward the bottom of the gauge. *Nuts!*

Though ground radar would show the aircraft passing the outer marker at this point, it's obvious that the pilot has been left struggling in limbo several miles farther back. He has been unable to keep up with the airplane, and the flight may be heading for trouble.

Golden Rules

No pilot gets "instrument airplane" tacked onto his or her license until the mandate, *Stay ahead of the aircraft,* is indelibly imprinted on the psyche and it is clearly understood that though navigation signals can be twisted like wet macaroni and weather forecasts can take on the substance of a politician's promise, one thing is for sure: *Attitude plus power equals performance.*

The elevator to these high plateaus is inscribed with three simple words: *Know your aircraft!* There's no getting around it. You may know the systems cold, but how can you achieve the desired performance from an aircraft unless you know the proper attitude and power settings? The pilot in our example didn't know how to extract the appropriate performance and became distracted by a gauge that "didn't look right." As a result, his airplane got away from him.

The information which can help prevent such scenarios cannot be found in the flight manual, alone. But it can easily be gathered during a relatively short VFR flight and assembled in what I call a "cheat sheet." I use them in all of the aircraft I fly (semi)regu-larly, and the notes have proved helpful.

There are no rules for developing a cheat sheet. To be useful, they should provide the information you think you would need quickly in a pinch. By describing my personal strategy and preferences (at least, as they applied to the recent gathering of information on a Piper Turbo Arrow), I hope only to provide some ideas that may help you in developing your own notes.

Getting Started

There are certain items I try to get on all lists: power and pitch settings for normal approach airspeeds; important limiting speeds that are not marked on the airspeed indicator or on readable placards in the cockpit; weight and fuel-consumption figures; "normal" gauge readings; and electrical load-shedding guidelines.

I also like to have handy the type of emergency information that doesn't bear committing to memory but also cannot wait until the flight manual is retrieved and consulted. For instance, my cheat sheets always show the airspeed that will provide best glide performance, should the engine suddenly go quiet, and the still-air distance the aircraft will travel for every 1,000 feet of altitude that is lost.

The power settings that will yield maneuvering speed at gross

PARO/A (38V)

KIAS @ 2,400 rpm	MP	pitch
120...gear up, level	25.5	0
120...gear dn, 640 fpm	27.0	5
120...gear dn, 1,000 fpm	23.0	10
100...gear up, level	20.0*	0
100...gear dn, 540 fpm	17.0*	4
100...gear dn, 1,000 fpm	15.0*	10

    *Add 1" MP for flaps 10
    1" MP = 5 KIAS or 100 fpm

Vy 97 KIAS— 8 dg
Vx 79 KIAS—12 dg

cruise climb 33"/2,450 rpm
105 KIAS—3 dg
120 KIAS—1 dg

Vle 133	Vlo 133 up	Vref 75
	111 dn	

GW 2,900 lbs   CHT btwn "D" @ "T"
fuel 432 lbs   oil press. middle of green
84 pph @ 75% (100° ROP)   vac press. 5.0 in.

Va 124 KIAS at gross (2,900 lbs) 27"/2,400 rpm
  -3 KIAS/100 lbs

best glide 95 KIAS 1.6 nm/1,000 ft
(lock override!)

Loads: (alt—65 amp; batt 25 amp/hr)

    55 amps (everything but heater and a/c)
    35 amps (everything above minus nav and ld lts)

25 LDG motor	10 ldg lt	5 ADF/MBR
20 a/c blower	10 nav lts	5 radio lts
20 pitot heat	8 nav/comm	5 DME
10 aux pump	5 ovhd lts	5 autopilot
10 strobes	5 pitch trm	5 txp

weight are also a "must." An indication of how much the airspeed should be reduced for every 100 pounds below gross weight also is nice to know in a pinch. To help keep tabs on the aircraft's weight (as well as time left in the tanks), maximum gross weight and fuel consumption (in pounds per hour) at normal cruise settings are listed.

I also like to have some information readily available about the electrical system. My lists include "normal" loads I should expect to see during night and day flights on the gauges, the battery's amp/hour rating and hints on load-shedding, should I have to depend exclusively on the battery.

Attitude Plus Power

By far, the information I use most and have found most helpful is the approach power settings. They go at the top of the list. As you can see from the list I developed for a Turbo Arrow, I like to have power and pitch settings for two approach airspeeds: 120 and 100 KIAS (both of which are included in the conversion tables on Jeppesen charts).

It is a great help when flying the Arrow to see at a glance that about 20 inches and 2,400 rpm will work just fine for the initial approach, or that about 25.5 inches will keep the controller reasonably happy if he wants me to keep the speed up.

The approximate power settings required to slide down a glide slope or quickly swoop down to the minimum descent altitude are there, too. Changes in loading and temperature may require some adjustments, but I've got the base lines established and have a good idea of what a

KIAS @ 2,400 rpm	MP	pitch
140...gear up, level	19	0
120...gear up, level	16	0
100...gear up, level	14*	0
100...gear dn, 640 fpm	14*	3
100...gear dn, 1,000 fpm	12*	3

*Add 1" MP for flaps 10
1" MP = 10 KIAS or 150 fpm

ENGINE-OUT: (use half rudder trim)

	MP	pitch
100...gear up, level	18	0
100...gear dn, 640 fpm	18	3
100...gear dn, 1,000 fpm	16	3

change of one inch in manifold pressure is going to do to indicated airspeed in level flight or to descent rate when headed downhill.

During a takeoff in poor visibility or into a low ceiling, the attitude indicator is my greatest ally. So, it's nice to know that about eight degrees nose-up should give me best rate-of-climb speed with takeoff power set.

Pitch settings for cruise climb also are there. (Piper recommends 105 KIAS, but I prefer 120 KIAS, which yields a shallower deck angle and more cooling air flowing around that hot-headed Continental, as well as an adequate 500-fpm climb.)

It may be days or months before I fly this particular airplane again. But when I do, I may want to compare instrument readings with known values. On my last few flights, cylinder head temperature stayed between the D and the T ("CYL HEAD TEMP" is inscribed in the middle of the gauge and the letters serve as the only solid references between the temperature limits marked on each side of the arc), oil pressure remained within the middle of the green arc and vacuum pressure registered five inches. If I see any big changes from these values, I'll know the system bears extra attention.

Shedding the Load

Similarly, if the ammeter reading isn't close to 35 during a day flight (with the navigation and landing lights off) or 55 at night (with the lights on), I'll be alert to a potential electrical system problem.

I would use the markings on circuit breakers as rough guidelines for load-shedding (actual draws will be a bit less) should the alternator fail. But, since they were much faded in the Arrow, I copied them onto my cheat sheet for ready reference.

Typically, I'll decide what I want to include on the cheat sheet for a certain aircraft while studying the flight manual. Then, I'll work out a checklist for obtaining the information during a short VFR flight.

If it's a twin, I'll kill two birds with one stone and copy the figures I want during a refresher flight with a multiengine instructor. The cheat sheet for the Piper Seminole will be worth its weight in enriched uranium if (Heaven forbid!) I ever need to shoot an instrument approach some day with only one powerplant to help out.

Though I've dubbed mine "cheat sheets," the practice of assembling potentially useful information in a ready source certainly isn't new. Unfortunately, few pilots seem to bother. And that's a shame, because the information can come in mighty handy in a pinch. It can mean the difference between staying ahead of, or falling behind the aircraft. u

One of the biggest dangers to an instrument pilot's decision-making capability is distraction. After all, single-pilot IFR is inherently distracting.

En route, with everything just cruising along, it might be less of a problem...but it can still bite the unwary.

Often, the distraction comes in the form of an interruption to your routine, which ought to include keeping a good scan going.

Here we have Brian Jacobson with some tips on how to avoid falling into the fixation trap.

Overcoming the Fixation Trap

lying an aircraft on instruments requires the ability to perceive information from several different sources, mentally process the information to decide if any action is required and then to react accordingly.

If a breakdown occurs anywhere in this process, smooth and accurate control of the aircraft will suffer. If the problem is serious enough, the safety of flight could be affected.

One of the keys to good instrument flying is how well a pilot scans his or her instruments and creates a mental picture of the aircraft's relationship with the ground. The faster a pilot is able to complete a scan and start another, while understanding the information presented and reacting appropriately, the more competent he will be at flying on the gauges.

I like to think of each instrument as one frame in a motion-picture film. Instead of being projected on a screen, the frames which bear the raw information are sent, one by one, directly to the pilot's brain for interpretation. The quicker the frames are received and assimilated, the quicker the pilot can "see the big picture."

Problems arise when a pilot *fixates*, or stares at one instrument. Fixation is caused by many factors, all relating to the experience level of the pilot, his confidence in himself and other physiological and psychological catalysts, such as fatigue and stress.

For example, a student instrument pilot can expect to fixate to some degree initially because he has not reached the point where comprehension of the continual changes reflected by the various gauges comes rapidly.

But as he gains experience and understanding of the instruments, he will learn that his scanning rate must accelerate. Until that happens, it is up to the instructor to watch for signs of fixation and to point them out to the student. As he progresses, the student will begin to scan more rapidly and better understand what he is seeing.

Lures to the Trap

The psychological makeup of a pilot will have a direct influence on his instrument flying. If he lacks confidence in himself or harbors fear or anxiety about his ability to fly on instruments, his scanning rate will suffer.

As the pilot falls behind the aircraft, he will tend to fixate on one instrument at the expense of others.

Physiological factors, such as illness, the use of medication or alcohol, fatigue, sleep loss and mild hypoxia, all have a bearing on a person's alertness and well-being. A pilot affected by one of these factors is likely to lose his concentration and find himself fixating on a primary instrument. Taken to an extreme, this could lead to the possibility that awareness of the information being provided by the other instruments is lost. A controlled descent into the terrain may result.

A low-time instrument pilot or one who barely maintains proficiency is more likely to fall into the fixation trap because of the lack of recent experience. There is no instructor aboard to point out the signs of fixation. Single-pilot IFR requires the ability to recognize the signs and to correct the instrument scan before events get out of control.

Whether flying VFR or IFR, a pilot must always monitor his mental state, because it determines how much he is able to concentrate on flying the aircraft. On the gauges, the pilot must focus all of his physical and mental faculties on the task at hand.

A pilot who is distracted by business matters, personal problems or other concerns in his life will not fly well. This is when fixation occurs, and the pilot focuses only part of his attention on just one instrument. When a pilot stares at one instrument for a period of time, other instruments will indicate that the flight is not going as intended.

Missed Messages

For instance, a pilot who fixates on the attitude indicator during an ILS approach will not notice that the localizer and, possibly, the glide slope indicators are showing that the aircraft is wandering from where it should be.

Another pilot, or an instructor, aboard the aircraft will recognize these deviations and the lack of any corrective action as evidence that the flying pilot or the student is fixating.

A student instrument pilot who does not take immediate corrective measures may either lack basic knowledge about flying an ILS approach or simply be scanning the instruments too slowly (i.e., spending too much time looking at each one). However, if the student or a rated instrument pilot in similar circumstances continues the approach while showing no recognition that it is not progressing as intended, it is likely that he is fixating.

As already mentioned, there are several reasons a pilot might fixate. One cause is an unexpected instrument indication. For instance, the pilot may stare at the altimeter after finding that it is reading a couple hundred feet higher than the target altitude. The pilot may focus his attention on the gauge while wondering how it got that far off. Meanwhile, other flight parameters suffer. Heading may wander. Airspeed may decay. A fault annunciator may go unnoticed.

I remember having had difficulty back when I was a student instrument pilot with climbing or descending turns on the gauges. I tended to focus on the heading indicator while rolling out on a new heading and usually would "bust" the assigned altitude. With practice and more experience in scanning all of the instruments, I was able to level the aircraft and roll out on my new heading at the same time.

Proficiency in scanning comes with experience, but even a seasoned instrument pilot who regularly flies in the system may have his concentration robbed by physiological or psychological factors to the point where he feels good about what he is doing even though the flight is going terribly wrong.

There are no statistics showing the degree to which fixation is involved in aircraft accidents. The absence of cockpit voice recorders and flight data recorders in light aircraft make such a determination nearly impossible.

However, recorders retrieved from the wreckage of several air carrier aircraft have clearly pointed to fixation. For example, a Boeing 707 accident that occurred in 1987 demonstrates the possible consequences when a pilot fails to scan all of his instruments and keep himself aware of the progress of a flight.

Following a False Cue

The 707 was on a night cargo flight from Wichita to Kansas City. There were embedded thunderstorms along the route, and the weather at Kansas City International was lousy: 200 overcast and a half mile visibility in fog.

Approach control vectored the aircraft to the localizer for the ILS Runway 1 approach and cleared it to continue its descent to 2,400 feet. The crew was told to maintain that altitude "until established" on the localizer and glide slope.

However, the captain failed to stop at 2,400 feet and continued the descent until the 707 hit trees on top of a ridge about three miles from the runway. The first officer did not advise the captain that he had descended below the assigned altitude, nor apparently did he cross-check his own instruments. If he had, he would have determined that the 707 was descending well below the glide slope.

In this case, the captain's attention apparently was fixed on the flight director system. Investigators learned that the captain knew the system very well and used it often. One pilot who flew with the captain said he sometimes would concentrate on the flight director so intently that he did not appear to notice raw data provided by other instruments, which would include the localizer and glide slope deviation indicators.

A very sophisticated attitude indicator, the flight director in the 707 used two command bars to provide vertical and horizontal steering cues. It could, for instance, provide steering information for the localizer and glide slope. It appears, however, that the captain never armed the system's glide slope capture mode and kept flying the pitch command bar as it had been set for the descent from cruise altitude, not knowing that the glide slope had not been captured.

Had he looked at the instrument directly below the flight director, the horizontal situation indicator, he would have known instantly that something was wrong with the approach—that the aircraft was descending far below the glide slope.

We'll never know why the highly experienced captain relied so heavily on the flight director, when there was so much more information available that would have alerted him to the fact that the aircraft was not where he thought it was. Perhaps, he was depending on his copilot to provide more information than he did. Perhaps, there was a psychological or physiological factor that affected his performance. Though none was mentioned in the accident report, it is obvious that the crew was under a great deal of stress: As the aircraft passed the outer marker, a new ATIS broadcast called the ceiling at 100 feet and visibility at one half mile—below minimums for the approach. (If the aircraft had not passed the marker, the crew would have been required by regulation to abort the approach.)

Escaping the Trap

It is difficult for a pilot to recognize that he is fixating, because, like the 707 captain, he may feel confident that all is proceeding normally. However, should you realize that you are fighting the controls to keep the aircraft in the proper attitude or on heading, be alert for fixation. Regroup and start your scan all over, forcing yourself to stay alert.

During an approach, when things seem to be going well, don't rely on any one instrument for guidance. Continue to scan and interpret all of the instruments. Call your progress along the approach out loud, if alone, or to yourself, if you have passengers. Track your altitude in relation to your decision height or minimum descent altitude.

The more alert you are while conducting an approach or another high-concentration maneuver, the more you reduce the chances of falling into the fixation trap.

Your best weapon is avoidance. If you are tired or not feeling well, leave the flying for another day. Your ability to scan your instruments will decrease as the day gets longer. Whenever eye/brain coordination slows, it is prime time for the fixation trap.

One way to avoid the trap is to jolt your brain back to activity before attempting an approach or some other task that requires considerable concentration.

Study the approach plate carefully. Force yourself to interpret the information, rather than just look at it, especially if you are very familiar with the approach. Pay particular attention to the critical altitudes and crossing fixes. Look at the airport diagram and do the same.

Then study the low-altitude or area chart and how you will be routed to the approach. Make sure you understand the relationship between your position and the final approach course.

I have found that, especially after a long leg which provides little inducement for mental activity, this method stimulates my eye/brain coordination. Also important is to develop a method of scanning the instruments in your panel and to use that "scanning plan" constantly. Let it become automatic. Not only will your instrument flying be smoother, but the chances of fixating on one instrument will be decreased considerably.

Never allow any instrument to attract more of your attention than any other during a critical phase of flight. Keep the scan going and be alert for any indication that an approach is not proceeding as it should. In that way, you can avoid the fixation trap.

As we learned from the Cessna crash described in the first section, just having an instrument rating does not mean you're prepared for flight into IMC.

Say you're flying VFR, and the weather starts to turn nasty. You have to decide how to deal with it. If you're really ready, you can simply file and proceed. But if you're not, and the weather forces you to go on the gauges, you've got a heap of trouble. Here's Brian Jacobson on how to make sure you're ready.

When VFR Won't Hack It

Pilots are taught early in their training the differences between visual and instrument flying conditions. As a pilot progresses into advanced certificates and ratings, even more emphasis is placed on the differences. Yet, too often, pilots continue VFR flights into adverse weather and become statistics in the NTSB's files.

The experience levels of pilots who get involved in this type of accident vary. Recently, a commuter airline captain flew into mountainous terrain while pressing a VFR flight into IFR conditions. He knew his way around the area well and apparently thought the terrain in which he eventually crashed was behind him. The weather conditions existing at the time were not forecast to be as bad as they were. There is no question that this pilot intentionally flew into IFR conditions without a clearance and that, at no time, did he attempt to obtain one.

Each pilot must have criteria established for deciding whether completion of a flight is possible under visual flight rules. For the non-instrument-rated pilot, this may mean canceling a flight before starting, turning back upon encountering unexpected IFR conditions or landing at an alternate airport along the way to wait out the weather.

An instrument-rated pilot who expects some weather along the way may file an IFR flight plan which he can activate prior to the point where he is expecting the inclement weather. Or, upon seeing weather ahead, he may call the controller whose airspace he is in and request an IFR clearance.

There are, however, some considerations before tackling the instrument conditions. One is that the aircraft must meet the requirements for IFR flight. Otherwise, there is no choice but to wait until the route is clear of any adverse weather.

Knowing What's Ahead

An instrument pilot who becomes aware of unforecast instrument conditions should not request an IFR clearance until he understands what type of weather is in front of him.

For example, suppose that during a weather briefing before takeoff the pilot is advised of a cold front well to the west of his route of flight. He is told that it is slow-moving and should not affect his trip. Once underway, however, the pilot sees that there's unexpected weather ahead. What he should do at this point is to call Flight Service and determine if that cold front has picked up steam or if some other phenomenon is generating the weather. Severe weather can be found ahead of or along a fast-moving cold front. Once in the clouds, it would be difficult to make that determination without airborne weather radar.

If you encounter IFR conditions along your route, try to avoid calling for a clearance into a TCA or other high-density airspace unless you have a flight plan already filed. Many times, the controllers will be too busy to put a flight plan in the system for you and will tell you to call Flight Service and get one on file. That would mean remaining VFR while you called Flight Service and filed, and then waited for the flight plan to get into the system and for the controller to get around to issuing you the clearance.

If you get into the clouds without a clearance, you have no idea how many other airplanes may be in the airspace around you. They could be climbing and descending through your altitude. Remember, the whole premise of the IFR system is that *no one* gets into the clouds or areas of poor visibility in controlled airspace without a clearance.

I once flew with a pilot in a Beech Baron from Fort Lauderdale to Fort Myers, Florida. It was a moonless night and very dark over the Everglades. Flying at 1,500 feet, we encountered the low scud that often appears in that area. The pilot turned the strobes off and the autopilot on, and kept going.

I asked him about getting an instrument clearance. He said he didn't know how to get one in the air. I picked up the mike and called for a clearance, and we completed the flight IFR.

The pilot apparently figured there wouldn't be any traffic over the Everglades. That type of thinking can kill you and others who become victims of your poor judgment.

Air-Filing

How do you get a clearance in the air?

It is a matter of knowing whose airspace you are in. If you are getting VFR advisories or flight-following service, advise the controller that you need an IFR clearance to continue.

If you are not already talking with ATC, check your IFR chart for the nearest center frequency. Both Jeppesen and NOS charts place the sector frequencies in boxes and identify them with the name of the center that controls that airspace.

IFR charts also contain approach control communication information. When flying near a terminal area, you will find the appropriate approach control frequency on one of the side panels of the chart. Even if you are not in that controller's airspace but he is able to identify you, he will tell you what frequency to use to get an IFR clearance.

The best options for a non-instrument-rated pilot are to call Flight Service while remaining VFR or to land at an alternate airport and give them a call on the telephone. Get an update on the conditions that are developing. You may have to wait out the weather before continuing. Or, if it is only local in nature, you may be able to fly around it to reach your destination, albeit a little later than originally planned. On the other hand, you might decide to return to your starting point and make the trip another day, in better weather.

One of the biggest risks facing a non-instrument-rated pilot on a long cross-country is getting caught on top of a solid layer of clouds. Before committing yourself to fly above clouds, be sure that you will be able to get down when you reach your destination.

Remember that forecasts are just that. There is no guarantee that you will find the promised weather upon arrival. Make sure you have a way out and that you have enough fuel aboard to make it.

When flying either VFR or IFR, I check the weather conditions along the route at least every two hours—more often than that if I suspect deteriorating conditions. I make sure that I ask the briefer for any amendments to forecasts I had been given earlier.

If a forecast is revised in the middle of a forecast period, anything is possible. I have found that amended forecasts usually reflect what is already occurring.

Don't Fake It

Recently, while on my way from Middletown, Pa. to Flint, Mich., I heard a Bonanza pilot call Erie Approach Control for an IFR clearance. The controller asked if the pilot was instrument-qualified.

The reply was a hesitant "Uh, yes." The controller promptly issued a clearance to Erie and gave the pilot vectors to one of the ILS approaches. About a minute after the pilot was cleared for the approach, he asked, "What is the localizer?"

After a short discussion about what the pilot meant, the controller advised him of the localizer frequency and once again cleared him for the approach. Shortly after that, the pilot radioed, "I should have the airport in sight, but I don't see it yet."

The controller's concern was obvious as he told the pilot, "The tower has cleared you to land. Call them on 118.1." A few seconds later, the pilot was back on the approach control frequency, saying he couldn't get the tower. The controller cleared him to land again and told him to remain on his frequency. After touchdown, the pilot switched over to the tower frequency.

A lot of questions come to mind when I hear an exchange like that. Is the pilot really instrument-rated? Is he current and qualified? Does he have instrument plates and charts aboard the aircraft? In this case, I wondered if the pilot tuned through the navigation frequency band, searching for the localizer.

The weather around the area was generally VFR, except for pockets of snow showers. Had he waited a while, he probably could have landed at Erie in VMC.

Escape Strategies

What should you do if you get caught on top of an overcast or inadvertently stumble into IMC during a VFR flight?

If you are on top and can maintain VFR for the time being, contact a flight service station or Flight Watch on 122.0 MHz and find out where the nearest conditions exist that will allow a safe, VFR descent.

If you cannot get that far because of fuel limitations, don't descend into the clouds hoping to break out below. One pilot I knew did just that and hit a house, killing himself and his son.

Call the local approach or center controller and explain your problem. He will help you get down while keeping IFR traffic away from you.

When encountering conditions that force you to descend to maintain VFR, be prepared to make a 180-degree turn back to where you came from when you reach a predetermined minimum altitude—say, 1,000 feet above the highest surrounding terrain.

If you find yourself in the soup and on the gauges, don't descend any farther. Remember the "four C's": climb, communicate, confess and comply. Climb to an altitude that will permit both safe passage over the terrain and use of your radio. Communicate with ATC. If you are not already talking with a controller, dial in 121.5 MHz and call for help. Confess your predicament to the controller who answers your call. Comply with the instructions he or she gives you.

The downside to calling ATC when caught on top or in IMC is that you probably will hear from the FAA later. If you don't have a good reason for being there, it may be difficult to avoid action being taken against you. But even enforcement action is better than crashing into a mountain, house or some other object that you never saw.

Years ago, one of my neighbors went flying with a non-instrument-rated pilot and two other friends. It was Thanksgiving Day, and they were just going sightseeing. But the weather was IFR and the pilot obtained a special VFR clearance out of the control zone. Shortly after takeoff, they got lost in the fog and crashed at the 600-foot level of a 2,000-foot mountain. All four were killed.

"Special" VFR

Special VFR can be useful at times, but a pilot must choose the *right* time for using it.

I have established personal limitations. I will only ask for a special

VFR clearance when the conditions requiring it are local in nature and not a part of a widespread weather system. I will not take off under special VFR when there's low visibility *and* a low ceiling (as my neighbor's pilot did).

For example, one airport I used to fly out of is a thousand feet above sea level, and the surrounding terrain rises about 400 feet. If the airport was reporting 800 feet and 10 miles, I knew the ceiling around the rest of the area would be about 1,400 feet with good visibility. Or, if we had something like two miles' visibility in haze and no ceiling, I would use a special VFR.

These conditions prevailed in the summer, and I would be certain to watch the temperature/dew point spread, especially around sunset, knowing that haze could turn to fog.

A pilot must plan a way out of any adverse condition that may arise during a flight. Preparing for a bad change in the weather makes sense. A pilot with an instrument rating has more options than a non-instrument-rated pilot. However, no matter how many words there are on his or her certificate or how many hours in the logbook, any pilot who attempts to continue in the face of adverse weather without having knowledge of the conditions ahead, the proper equipment and the personal ability to safely negotiate the conditions is a good candidate to be the subject of an NTSB accident file.

We'll close this capter with an article on one of the more dangerous things that can happen to in instrument pilot during the en route portion of the flight: getting into an unusual attitude.

When in VFR, we have the distinct advantage of being able to see the horizon and therefore orient ourselves. But in the soup, an unusual attitude can be, and often is, a killer.

Here again is Bill Kelly, who has experienced unusual attitudes more than most of us have in his test pilot work.

Recovering from Unusual Attitudes

Imagine that you and your CFI are flying along straight and level in good weather. Then, after a quick warning from your instructor, you find yourself in a steep bank, with the nose 30 degrees below the horizon.

Recover! Try not to exceed Vno (maximum operating speed). By all means, stay below Vne (never exceed speed). Don't exceed 3.8 G. Don't let the engine and prop overspeed.

That's what a pilot usually is presented with during a biennial flight review that I am administering. Typically, there's a pre-briefing on recovering from unusual attitudes. The air work is always done in good daylight weather but, sometimes, with the pilot under the hood and the attitude and direction indicators covered.

The warning is: "Close your eyes. Let go of the controls. When I say so, open your eyes and recover."

Common Error

One of the most common errors I've seen pilots make is failing to adjust the throttle, even when the nose is low and airspeed is increasing.

That power lever has got to come to idle, right now. To heck with concerns about shock-cooling the engine. If airspeed is building rapidly, power has to be cut quickly.

Just the opposite holds, of course, if it's a nose-high unusual attitude. Go to full power, pronto, and try to keep the airspeed above the one-G stall speed value. Keep the angle of attack (AOA) below stall angle by easing forward on the control wheel—almost to zero G.

If a nose-high, decreasing airspeed situation is not handled promptly and correctly, it will likely turn into a graveyard spiral or a spin. Recovery will certainly be from a nose-low, high-speed condition, which could shed your wings.

So, how do you make that high-speed recovery?

Reduce power and level the wings. Don't try to get the nose back up to the horizon until bank has been reduced to zero. Use coordinated aileron and rudder pressure to roll the wings level. You might want to hold a little forward pressure on the control wheel so that G load doesn't build during the roll-out.

A graveyard spiral could develop if you try to get the nose up while still in a steep, descending turn. Up-elevator may only increase the G loading and speed as the nose drops even further. Bank angle may get even steeper. Airspeed, G load and engine rpm (with a fixed-pitch prop) will go past all limits. The wings and parts of the empennage might be found by investigators far from the big hole dug by the fuselage and engine.

Be careful, too, that you don't roll rapidly out of the steep, descending bank while you're pulling high G at a high airspeed. That's called a "rolling pullout" and *really* loads the wing.

But, very often, that's just what I see when even experienced pilots recover from one of the relatively mild nose-low unusual attitudes that I set up for them in training.

Discussions of unusual attitudes usually evoke casual dismissals, such as: "No decent pilot would let his airplane get into such a situation." Or: "A good instrument pilot flies attitude and never gets into steep banks."

Sure. But lots of airplanes *do* crash each year from out-of-control turning descents. We *are* talking about the "real world" here.

Spiral Divergence

And that world includes a phenomenon called "spiral divergence." Any airplane can exhibit the phenomenon. It occurs when the airplane gets beyond a particular bank angle and won't tend to roll back to wings-level all by itself.

An airplane in a shallow left turn tends to carry a little left sideslip angle. The nose isn't quite following the turn, and relative wind is slightly from the left side. (Vice versa for right turns, of course.) Light airplanes have a small amount of effective dihedral, created primarily from the angle at which the wings attach to the fuselage and/or by a swept leading edge.

That effective dihedral provides a rolling moment away from the sideslip. It tends to roll the plane back to level from a shallow bank. Dihedral effects assist you in holding the wings level. They permit you to make shallow turns with just the rudder pedals while you are busy unfolding a chart.

But once you get past 10 to 20 degrees of bank, the airplane probably won't recover to wings-level by itself. Past about 30 degrees, most airplanes will tend to *increase* the bank angle.

Now, we are into spiral divergence. The turn radius is decreased sufficiently that the outboard wing is moving with a measurably higher airspeed than the wing on the inside of the turn. Because of the unbalanced lift, the airplane wants to roll even steeper. If you haven't added sufficient up-elevator to maintain a vertical component of lift equal to weight, you start to descend.

That increasing descent in our left turn means that, initially, the airplane is also slipping left. Now, directional stability is stronger than dihedral and the airplane wants to point its nose into the relative wind. So, the nose yaws left. But in this steep left bank, left is also *down*. So, the nose drops and speed increases. And even without any additional up-elevator, G load increases due to the effect of the elevator (or stabilator) trim setting.

Now, it's probably too late to recover by using only up-elevator. Any nose-up command is only going to tighten the turn, increase the G, allow the nose to drop further and cause the airspeed to build even further.

You have to roll the wings level and get the power to idle before the wings are torn off or, if it's nighttime or you're in clouds, before the attitude indicator tumbles.

Deadly Slowdown

Now, let's consider some scenarios that could set up a graveyard spiral.

Imagine an inexperienced pilot or one who's current on instruments but not really proficient and needs work on his scan. Take your pick: a dark night; instrument conditions; daylight with haze obscuring the horizon; even worse, haze over calm water.

The Bugbuster normally cruises at 120 knots and stalls at about 60. The pilot is concerned about turbulence or is trying to dodge clouds in the hazy murk. Maybe he's lost and decides to conserve fuel while he searches for a recognizable landmark. In any case, he reduces power and retrims for 80 knots.

That slowdown could be deadly.

Our pilot—let's call him Jack—gets real busy reading charts, tuning the nav radios or talking on the comm. He trimmed the elevator for 80 knots but didn't trim the rudder. (If the Bugbuster is a single, it probably doesn't have rudder trim but is rigged for straight flight at normal cruise speed and power.)

While Jack is busy in the cockpit, the left wing slowly begins to drop. There's no clear horizon, and the change doesn't register on his peripheral vision. A spiral is starting. And the nose-up trim is going to get Jack into trouble.

He thought he had trimmed for an airspeed—80 knots. But in reality, trim (just like the elevator, itself) changes the AOA.

Sure, his nose-up trim sets the plane for 80 knots—but only in wings-level, one-G flight. But, once the spiral starts, the higher AOA is going to cause a tighter turn, more G, more airspeed and, perhaps, the wing to separate from the fuselage.

There's a good chance that the low-speed, level trim is good for six G at 200 knots in a runaway spiral—and without any further elevator input from the pilot.

Next time you're up for some air work, set up the airplane for slow flight and, then, take your hands off and let it wander. Put a little pressure on a rudder pedal, as if you inadvertently did so while reaching for something in the back seat.

Watch how quickly that spiral develops, how rapidly airspeed, bank angle, and G increase, even with hands and feet off the controls.

Before speed and G load get excessive, roll back to wings-level and note how fast the nose pitches up way above the horizon because of the trim. A nose-high unusual attitude might mean a stall and spin.

Moral? Don't trim for slow flight unless you really have to and you can devote full time to the instruments or a visual horizon.

The purpose for reducing power if you find your airspeed building rapidly is to slow the rate of buildup.

But suppose you fly behind a fixed-pitch prop? You had better be real concerned about not flinging a prop blade (or the engine).

Most fixed-pitch propellers nearly reach redline rpm at full-throttle airspeed in level flight. They reach redline rpm, also, just above redline airspeed with the throttle at idle.

Dump Your Lift

Let's get back to a subject we've skirted: nose-high unusual attitudes.

Unless you're practicing aerobatic maneuvers or let a nose-low recovery take itself nose-high or mishandle a big power addition in an airplane that's sensitive to that, there's no tendency for a nose-high divergence.

But it could happen—and does happen on check rides.

My recommendation for recovery is to forget the existing bank angle. Don't try to level the wings just yet. Go to full power and move the control wheel forward. Dump your lift. Reduce the AOA. Make yourself light on the seat as you reduce G loading almost, but not quite, to zero.

Jack's Bugbuster stalls at 60 knots in level flight at max gross weight. If he dumps almost all of his wing lift, the Bugbuster's ailerons, elevator and rudder probably will still remain effective down to 20-30 knots. If his push on the wheel is enough to lower AOA way below the value for maximum coefficient of lift, the Bugbuster probably won't stall and spin.

But Jack had better not use a lot of aileron in an attempt to level the wings while the nose is still way up and airspeed is still very low. Adverse yaw from aileron deflection might start a big yaw rate that could lead to a spin.

Wild Ride

I recently experienced a variety of unusual attitudes while riding with a friend, "Tommy," in a clip-wing Cub.

Tommy did a good job with lazy eights and chandelles. But he had received no formal aerobatic training, and his barrel rolls were a little sloppy.

One time, he didn't get the nose high enough before starting the roll, and the roll rate was too slow. The nose was way below the horizon before we had rolled 180 degrees.

We were in a screaming, rolling dive and trying to recover to level flight—a graveyard spiral coupled with a rolling pullout. Bad. I had to take over and make an immediate recovery. With only 120 degrees of the roll completed, the nose was already 20 degrees below the horizon and airspeed was building fast.

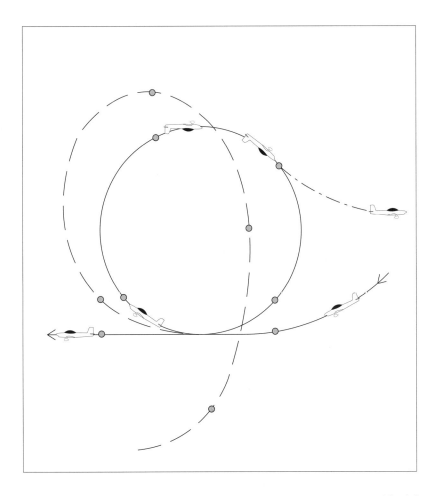

If you don't know what you're doing, aerobatics can get you into trouble. (1) Here, "Tommy" started a loop pulling only two G, when at least three G was needed. (2) At the top of the egg-shaped loop, Tommy should still have been pulling G but had no airspeed left. (3) Still pulling no G, Tommy's airspeed is building quickly. (4) Now, Tommy is in a vertical dive with airspeed going through the redline.

I recovered by immediately reducing power and *reversing* the direction of roll. Only 120 degrees of roll was needed to get back to wings-level flight. Had we continued to the right, 240 degrees of roll would have been needed. By then, the nose would have been almost straight down and the airspeed and tach needles would have passed their "pegs".

So, let's establish our first rule for recovering from nose-low unusual attitudes:

Rule 1: Roll the shortest direction to get to an upright, wings-level attitude.

Then, Tommy showed me a loop. I knew we were in trouble when the G-meter showed only two G's as we started the pull-up. Not enough G means a low pitch rate. And that meant we were going to run out of airspeed before getting over the top (see the accompanying drawing).

Sure enough, we fell out of the peak. The Cub came close to stalling. Wings level and inverted, the nose was dropping rapidly, way below the horizon. But still no G. Tommy wasn't pulling enough on the stick, and we were heading for a high-speed vertical dive.

Again, in the interest of self-preservation, I grabbed the control stick and throttle. I pulled the throttle to idle and rolled rapidly to an upright, wings-level attitude.

When we recovered, the nose was only 45 degrees below the horizon, but the airspeed had almost touched Vne. Had Tommy continued his "loop," we would have had to pitch through 135 degrees with airspeed and rpm beyond the limits.

Rule 2: Don't make a split-S recovery. Roll the shortest direction to upright, wings-level.

Tommy and I practiced some vertical maneuvers: loops, split-S's and Cuban 8's. We found that we had to pull at least three G at the start of a loop to reach the peak with sufficient airspeed and G available. And we had to apply considerable back stick coming over the top to keep a good pitch rate going so that we didn't get into a high-speed vertical dive.

Rule 3: Don't do aerobatics until you've had formal training, including spins and recoveries from unusual attitudes, with a qualified instructor.

Rule 4: Don't do aerobatics in a Normal or Utility category airplane.

Rule 5: Don't do aerobatics without a G-meter installed.

Spin Recovery

Now, let's consider another unusual attitude: the final phase of recovering from a spin—when autorotation has stopped, the nose is pointing almost straight down and airspeed is building quickly.

Recovery from this unusual attitude is often mishandled. Most pilots tend to pull too little G initially, and the airspeed gets way too high.

You have to get the wings level and apply sufficient G while the airspeed is still within bounds. Get the pitch-up to level flight started and, hopefully, completed while the airspeed is still within the green arc.

Your flight manual may include a statement such as: "Recovery from an inadvertent one-turn spin may consume as much as 1,000 feet of altitude."

Well, guess what? The test pilot who did those certification spins probably used about three G during the dive recovery. (How are *you* going to recognize three G without a G-meter?)

Your Normal category airplane is only guaranteed to 3.8 G, with maybe a 50 percent buffer. No wonder the placard states: "Intentional spins prohibited." A Normal category bird *can* recover from a one-turn spin. But it's very easy to overstress the airframe and overspeed the engine on recovery from the ensuing dive.

Some airplanes are certified in both the Normal and Utility categories, with spins permitted when operated according to the requirements for Utility work. Many of these airplanes don't really want to "stay" in a spin when they're within the required weight and balance limits. They tend to "self-recover"—break the stall. But what if the pilot tries for a four-turn spin by holding the elevator all the way back and full rudder into the spin?

Here's what I've seen during spin tests in various airplanes:

First, it's easy to miss just when the spinning stops unless you are watching some special instruments. They'll show airspeed starting to build rapidly, an increase in roll rate but a slowing of yaw rate.

You can't really see this through the windshield. The airplane appears to be pointing almost straight down and to still be rotating. It is—but mostly about the roll axis and less about the vertical (yaw) axis. A tail-damping stability factor makes full-up elevator less powerful than in non-turning flight, so the airplane may fly unstalled with the flippers full-up.

The real telltale is the G-meter. But not all Utility birds have one. The needle in the G-meter starts to move upwards, rapidly, as the spin turns into an extreme graveyard spiral.

You might go right past Va (maneuvering speed) with full-up (pro-spin) elevator and full pro-spin rudder. This is an extremely unusual attitude that puts extreme loads on the airframe.

Don't try even a one-turn spin in a Normal category airplane. And don't mess with spins in Utility or Acrobatic category airplanes without availing yourself of good instruction.

George's Tricks

Another way you could inadvertently find yourself in an unusual attitude is if, for some reason, something goes awry with your old buddy "George."

The autopilot has to be watched. It could lose gyro input and roll the airplane past design limits or short a diode and command full nose-up trim.

Almost any bad command an autopilot can give, however, can be overridden. But you have to be watching for them and know what to do. Every system has different operating procedures that have to be learned. You have to know, cold, all the methods of disconnecting good old George.

You should be able to manually override George on the controls without exerting too much force. But, keep in mind that if George has issued a nose-down command and you belay that order by pulling back on the yoke, you're also running the elevator trim servo towards full nose-down. Then, when you finally disconnect or the elevator servo clutch finally slips, you will be confronted by the full force of the trim tab.

Arm wrestling with George could get you into a wings-level vertical dive past Vne.

Good Exercise

Don't laugh at your CFI's attempts to confuse you with eyes-closed or even eyes-open unusual attitudes. Your instructor has to see how you react to moderate attitude excursions.

He or she has to give you exercise in prompt, rapid and correct responses to rather gentle excursions from controlled flight.

If you're instrument-rated, don't be insulted if your CFII recommends that you come back for more training on partial-panel procedures before he or she signs off your BFR.

Someday, you may be on your own to recover from an inadvertent extreme unusual attitude. And you might have to perform the recovery "partial panel," using that unreliable little devil, the turn coordinator.

Approach
and Landing

T he approach and landing get most of the attention
in both training and practice, and for good reason.
The workload on a pilot increases dramatically, and
a small mistake here can lead to disaster.

IFR pilots have special concerns, since they're often landing in bad weather
with high winds, slippery surfaces, or both.

We devoted an entire book to approaches, but they deserve another look.
Here's how to handle it when ATC forces you to switch approaches at the last
moment.

When ATC Throws a Curve

Surface winds were forecast to be from the northeast, so, fifty miles
from Nashville, you review the procedures for the ILS approach to
Runway 2L. Several miles later, ATIS confirms that 2L is the runway in
use. You review the plate once more and set your nav radios, confident
that you're now ready for the approach.

With about ten miles to go, the controller informs you, "This will be
radar vectors for the VOR/DME Runway 13 approach."

The adrenalin surges. You shift into high gear and scramble to find
the new approach plate as the aircraft rolls into a 45-degree bank and
the direction indicator swings off its mark.

The timing was inconvenient, to say the least. You were caught off
guard in the middle of pre-landing checks, slowing the airplane and
descending to the last assigned altitude. Moments like these are never
comfortable and, certainly, are not conducive to safety, particularly
during a single-pilot IFR flight.

Preparing for the approach ahead of time is important, but how do you cope with those unsettling, last-minute changes that throw any planning into total disarray? The answer is to develop an effective and rapid approach plate review strategy.

Head Start

If you use Jeppesen charts, begin well in advance by removing all of your destination airport approach plates from the binder. Include the runway diagram and any STARS (standard terminal arrival routes).

With NOS charts, mark the destination section with bulldog or paper clips, so there will be a minimum of paper-flipping at the worst possible time.

If low IFR weather is anticipated, select the approach plates for your alternate, too, but keep them separate.

It's a good idea before your flight to double-check that you really do have the correct plates available. It sounds pretty basic, but mistakes can easily happen.

Jeppesen arranges its plates first by city, then by airport. Indianapolis, for example, has no fewer than seven different landing facilities listed under the same bold-face heading.

Begin your review prior to departure or early in your flight by looking over the runway diagram (a separate page in the Jeppesen arrangement but included on each NOS chart). This is crucial preparation for any approach, particularly for anticipating the "mystery procedure."

Familiarize yourself with the various runways. Then draw wind vectors in pencil, using the reported and forecast surface winds. This will help you to visualize the runway that's currently favored and the one which might be preferable later on if conditions should change.

Also make a mental note of the airfield elevation. This will be important when reviewing the various approach procedures. Jeppesen publishes the field elevation on the top of each plate, as well as on the separate airport page. NOS charts show field elevation in a box on top of the airfield diagram.

To see how this would work, let's assume that Nashville is our destination and that a northeasterly wind favors landing on Runway 2. Before takeoff or during a quiet moment en route, we would evaluate how a wind shift would affect this planning. If the wind backs to the north, for instance, Runway 2 would still the best bet, but if it veers to a more easterly direction, Runway 13 might be favored. It would be wise, therefore, to consider the VOR/DME Runway 13 approach as a backup.

Even if the controller offers another approach at the last minute,

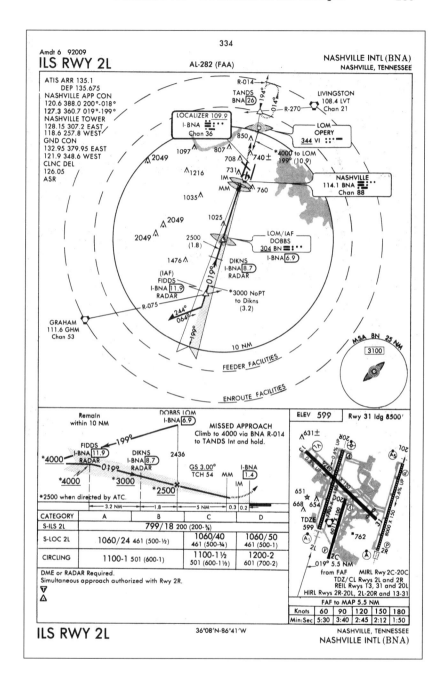

question him or her. If wind conditions appear favorable for the approach you've already prepared for, request it. The worst that can happen is your request will be refused. But you may be accommodated. It doesn't hurt to ask.

Checking the Highlights

Using a colored highlighter during the review process is essential. It will help to focus your attention when you scan the approach plate.

Start by highlighting the minimum safe altitude (MSA) for the arrival area. This number (or numbers for various sectors) appears at the top of a Jeppesen plate and to the right of center on an NOS chart. The MSA will give you an idea of obstruction and terrain heights in the airport neighborhood. It also may come in handy as an emergency minimum. In our example, the minimum safe altitude within a 25-mile radius of the outer marker for the ILS 2L approach is 3,100 feet.

Next, on the plan view (i.e., the "map"), note the highest obstructions in the airport vicinity (Jeppesen uses a fat arrowhead to point them out). In this case, the highest points are a trio of obstructions to the west of the airport. They're 2,049 feet high—or about 1,500 feet above airfield elevation. The MSA will keep you about 1,000 feet above them.

On both the Jeppesen and NOS charts, there are four frequencies shown in the plan view. Highlight the primary navaid frequency (that for the *ILS DME* on the Jepp and the *LOCALIZER* on the NOS), so there will be less opportunity for error when setting the radios later on. This is particularly important with VOR approaches when two nearby VORs can lead to confusion.

Highlight the inbound course so there is no mistake about the required track once the pressure starts building. Be sure to scan for any relevant notes.

On this chart, there are a number of DME fixes along the inbound course. With the amount of data on the plate, you will want a quick identification reference. Highlight the small mileage figures such as 11.9 at *FIDDS*, 8.7 at *DIKNS* and 6.9 at *DOBBS* to simplify the cross-check.

Now, let's move to the profile section. Again, scan for notes. In this case, either DME or radar is required to initiate the approach. If you do require radar assistance, mark this note with a highlighter so you don't forget to make the request.

The profile indicates that, once established on the charted procedure, you may descend to 4,000 feet. Highlight this number for quick reference. The profile view also indicates some step-down fixes in the event the glide slope cannot be acquired and a localizer-only approach is necessary.

The difficulty with step-down fixes is the confusion over where you are as your eye shifts between the plan and profile view. The simple solution is to highlight one section, such as *FIDDS* to *DIKNS*, both on the profile and on the plan view. This will help you make a rapid cross-check.

Altimeter Audit

One critical check during an ILS approach is the altimeter setting. After all, you will be descending to within 200 feet of the ground with increasingly reduced obstacle clearance limits along the approach.

At the *DOBBS* marker, there is a glide slope 2,436-foot altitude indication which should be highlighted. Check your altimeter as you pass the marker. If it varies more than 75 feet from 2,436, it may be judicious to double-check your altimeter setting or abandon the approach.

On this ILS, the localizer-only missed approach point is at the 1.4 DME fix. Vertically highlight this line to form a "stop bar" on the chart. This is another important quick-reference point if the glide slope fails and the approach becomes localizer-only.

The information to review next is the missed approach. Highlight only the turn direction, if any, the altitude (4,000 in this case) and the heading or radial (014). When making a quick scan on final, these highlighted numbers will zing into view as reminders.

Finally, let's look at the "minimums" section. In this case, we would highlight the decision height (799) and the appropriate minimum circling altitude (1,100, if our ground speed will be less than 121 knots), since we may be required at the last minute to land on another runway.

We didn't highlight the minimum descent altitude for the localizer-only approach for a reason: It could cause confusion during a full ILS approach. But if your glide slope flag were to appear, the un-highlighted MDA figure would be easy to spot.

Finally, highlight the descent rate (not available on NOS charts) and approach time corresponding with your anticipated ground speed. In the event the glide slope fails, timing may be required. Whether or not it is necessary, timing *every* approach is a very good habit to develop.

It is important, of course, to become familiar with all of the information on the approach charts ahead of time. But when the time comes, all that's necessary is to begin at the top of the plate and work down, scanning only the highlighted areas.

The highlight/scan procedure is simple and fast. By working some hypothetical examples at home, you can speed up your assessment time dramatically. Then, when ATC drops the unanticipated approach in your lap, you will be able to cope.

The key to handling the mystery approach is to develop and practice a quick-scan technique. For safety's sake, nothing is more beneficial than planning well in advance and anticipating and preparing for what is likely to happen.

Let's say you've made the approach and have to go around. The critical moment, from the standpoint of flying the airplane, is arresting your descent and beginning the most important part of the missed approach: the climb.

Here's Bill Kelly on how to execute the go-around safely.

Making Safe Go-Arounds

Instrument pilots have the idea of the go-around drilled into them as part of training. Always plan to make the missed approach, and all that. But sometimes we're not ready...or we need to go around after descending for landing.

Except on an instrument approach when the weather is at minimums or on a visual approach when there is still an airplane on the runway ahead, few pilots seem to consider that maybe a go-around will be needed. But every "arrival" should involve the conscious decision to either land or go around. *Land* only if everything is perfect as you get near the runway. Otherwise, *plan* to execute the go-around.

Especially on final approach, you have to do a little "defensive flying." At an uncontrolled airport, you ought to be ready, just in case that other guy holding short decides to pull out onto the runway. That happened to me last year, and it wasn't an old no-radio Cub, but a big turboprop twin. Probably, the crew had already switched to departure control and wasn't listening on unicom. They didn't bother to make a visual check of the final approach area.

It's not only other aircraft that you need to look out for. Several years ago, I barely missed colliding with a big buck deer at a Pennsylvania mountaintop airport surrounded by thick forest. It scared me more than the deer. I made a last-minute full-power grab for altitude and went right over the big rack of antlers. (I swear, those big brown Bambi eyes were laughing at me as I went overhead.)

More recently, an acquaintance had to send his propeller back to the prop shop after striking a Dalmatian hound. Amazingly, "Bosco" survived with only a skull fracture and a mild concussion. But one prop tip was bent beyond repair.

Wildlife is no joke when it comes to airplane damage. Anything bigger than a squirrel is likely to cause serious damage. And the smaller the critter, the harder it is to see. Better be practiced on the go-around maneuver before you go into a wilderness airstrip or Uncle Abner's cow pasture.

Watch out, too, for unorthodox methods some airport managers use to "close" their fields for light runway repairs or repainting. One I know of (a non-pilot type) litters the runway with sawhorses to supplement the standard painted "X". Some day, when the tower controllers are off duty, some pilot is going to "eat" one of those sawhorses—probably early one morning or just after dark, when the X's are hard to see.

Better read the notams and stay ready for a late go-around when you plan a flight to Podunk Regional.

Practice Pays

But you *aren't* going to make a *good* go-around if you haven't practiced the maneuver recently in the aircraft you're flying.

I'll bet that if you try to stay current in three different aircraft models, you occasionally practice landings in each one. Better practice that alternative, too—the go-around.

Each airplane is a little different when you pour the coal to it in the landing configuration. Some will exhibit very little pitch or longitudinal trim change. Others may pitch up rather violently. The "pusher" powerplant mounted atop a Lake amphibian, on the other hand, will try to nose you down sharply when you go to full throttle with landing approach trim. And many of the big, powerful singles need a *lot* of right rudder when you decide to go (almost *full* rudder in the T-tail Lance). The same is true for most big twins with non-counter-rotating props.

That go-around maneuver isn't quite the same as a normal takeoff. You are trimmed differently and probably have the flaps down past the takeoff setting. There isn't going to be much airspeed change, as on takeoff, but you will rapidly be changing from a descent to a climb. The go-around is really a special and separate maneuver, and it *does* require a little practice. Unfortunately, it isn't covered on many flight checks and BFRs. And the lack of proficiency shows up in the accident files.

For example, the files are loaded with pilots who shove the throttle and raise the landing gear almost simultaneously, then belly-land because they didn't ensure they were climbing before reaching for the gear lever. And pilots who "put the pedal to the metal" and retract the flaps at the same time, and settle into the turf in a stalled condition.

During a recent BFR in a Bonanza, we performed an "unsat" go-around from an ILS under the hood. It wasn't a missed approach, but resulted from a sudden call from the tower. "Break off your approach to the right—*now!*" We had conflicting traffic, and they wanted us out of there. We were in the standard ILS descent—almost three degrees—and getting close to decision height. The pilot started an immediate right turn, "popped" his Foggles, *then* added power and raised his nose. Not quite the right sequence. Had we really been in IMC, it could have been hairy. We got pretty low before the descending turn became a climbing turn-out.

Step by Step

Do not start any turns until the climb is established. For that matter, it's preferable not to start any turns until higher than 500 feet AGL. Starting that go-around turn while still in a descent usually means a steepened descent, a harder time getting the nose up to climb attitude and, maybe, a high angle of attack and close proximity to a stall.

The first two steps in *any* go-around, regardless of whether you're in IMC or VMC, are to go to *takeoff power* and, at the same time, *raise the nose.* Apply takeoff power and raise the nose to break the descent and start a climb. Don't turn and do *not* raise the gear or the flaps until the descent is stopped and a climb is started.

After those first two steps, follow the procedures in your aircraft flight manual (AFM). Gear, first, or flaps—whatever the AFM recommends. Of course, you should already have maximum rpm and full-rich mixture set; that's the only way you will get full power.

You do not want to find yourself on short final, in sudden need of maximum power, with the prop set to turn 200 rpm below maximum or with the mixture still leaned for cruise. When you have to get out of there, you want only to have to move the throttles to get maximum engine power. Lots of engines will "hiccup" at full throttle if the mixture isn't full-rich. And if the props are still set for 2,400 rpm, when max is 2,700, horsepower will be reduced almost by the same proportion as rpm-set to rpm-max.

A go-around from short final is no time to have to advance the mixture(s) and the prop(s) before you dare jam the throttle(s) forward. A half-mile out there on final approach is the absolute *latest* to have the mixtures and props set for the possible go-around.

In almost all of the airplanes you and I fly, the red knob(s) and blue knob(s) should be set full forward no later than abeam the downwind end of the runway on a visual approach or at the final approach fix on an instrument approach.

There are a few AFMs that advise using less than max rpm and a leaner than full-rich mixture until you either have to make a go-around or are about to touch down. That's just asking for trouble the first time you really have to "go" at the last minute.

Down and Dirty

Some of those AFMs make it seem that raising the landing gear is essential to getting any climb performance. Baloney on that, too!

That airplane was certified under CAR 3 or FAR 23 as able to climb at an acceptable rate with the gear still dangling—even with full flaps (unless the flaps can be retracted in two seconds or less, as allowed by the Cherokee manual flap lever, for example). FAR 23.77 requires that an airplane achieve a 1-30 climb angle at sea level with *everything* hanging (except for rapid-retract flaps).

So, don't be in a rush to clean up the airplane. Get the power all the way up and set the appropriate pitch attitude. *Then* worry about the gear and flaps. But don't just "dump" those flaps to full-up. Follow the AFM here. Your manual might recommend raising the flaps only to 10 or 20 degrees extended initially. Or it may call for "milking" them to full-up.

Even an old high-wing Cessna with its barn doors all the way down to 40 degrees extension will still fly, if a bit precariously, at least level with full power. (However, it might be a good idea to delay going past 20 or 30 degrees extension until landing is assured and you are sure the runway is clear.)

Somewhat contrary to current FAA teaching, the use of full flaps doesn't really gain you much on a normal landing. You get lots more drag, sure, but almost no decrease in actual stall or touchdown speed. Full flaps may cause considerable nose-down pitch and necessitate lots of nose-up trim. That's trim you will be *sorry* you have made when you face a last-minute go-around.

Full flaps probably will provide a considerably steeper glide path on final. But who needs that with 3,000 or more feet of macadam ahead?

That extra flap extension will cost you dearly on a last-minute go-around. Why create a lot of extra drag if you don't need it for the runway you're using? Why not plan ahead and leave the airplane in a reasonable configuration for a possible go-around?

Extending unneeded flaps will probably give you more troubles if you encounter near-limit crosswind conditions at the runway. Check your AFM. Does it provide the flap setting used by the test pilot in chalking up the maximum demonstrated crosswind value? Probably not. He may have used only 10 degrees of flap, or none at all.

The point is to keep the airplane in the best possible configuration for a go-around. Sure, you have to have the wheels down. But you do not necessarily have to extend the flaps all the way.

If you're shooting an ILS to minimums, do *not* extend full flaps until you're out of the clouds and have the runway in sight. My preference is to keep the flaps at the recommended takeoff or approach setting, *at the most*, until ready to land. On a nonprecision or circling approach, why not leave the flaps *retracted* until you are on final approach for landing? It makes no sense to degrade your airplane's performance just to reduce the turn radius necessary to keep the runway in sight. It's not worth it.

On the Go

Enough generalizing; let's discuss the real thing. On aircraft carriers, a go-around is called a "wave-off." Those flat-tops have a big "lip" on the approach end of the runway—60-80 feet worth. As the ship pitches in high seas, that lip can rise right up through the glide path. When the LSO (landing signal officer) blinks the red lights, he means *climb now!* And you had better answer the wave-off *immediately*.

You should be ready to respond immediately to your own wave-off. Don't just perform a gentle transition from approach glide to a half-hearted climb. *Get out of there, now!*

You need to experiment and practice a little to get *your* wave-off technique perfected. And you don't have to be down low to do it. Climb a few thousand feet and "dirty-up" to final approach configuration. Experiment with both full and approach flaps. Set up and trim for a normal approach descent angle and normal approach airspeed. Have the mixture rich and prop lever full forward. Then, go rapidly to full throttle and simultaneously rotate the nose to go-around climb attitude.

As an approximation, pitch initially to about the same attitude you see during a normal lift-off or touchdown. Leave the gear and flaps down. Adjust the pitch attitude to give the desired "dirty" climb airspeed. If the AFM doesn't recommend one, you could shoot for Vx (best angle of climb airspeed) if it's not way below normal final approach speed. If Vx is that low, then just maintain the approach airspeed.

Memorize that pitch attitude—both as it appears when you look over the nose and as it's displayed on the attitude indicator.

Try the same maneuver again, this time with a more rapid pitch into the climb attitude. The object is to stop the descent quickly without encountering buffet or setting off the stall-warning horn (this is no time for an accelerated stall).

Then, investigate the configuration changes as you clean up the aircraft, preferably according to the procedures prescribed by the AFM.

Most general aviation airplanes require relatively little pitch trim change upon gear retraction, but the flaps may be quite a different story.

Get a feel for the airplane's reaction and amount of wheel force required to counter sudden flap retraction. If "Old Bessie" pitches up hard when you apply full throttle, then even harder when you retract the flaps, you may want to plan to re-trim *after* you add power and *before* you raise the flaps, especially at night or in the soup.

If you fly an early Aztec (a pre-"F" model), be ready for a hard pitch *down* when you raise the flaps. It could put you right into the ground if you aren't ready for it. (The Aztec F has an interconnect between flaps and stabilator trim; you get an "auto re-trim" when you extend or retract flaps.)

Also, check the VSI while you are struggling to climb "full dirty." If you can hold, say, 200 fpm at 60 KIAS, you are meeting the climb requirements of FAR 23. And 200 fpm probably is acceptable until you have gained enough clearance above the terrain to safely raise the flaps.

(A caution on a few homebuilts which have large flap areas and manual flap levers: They develop excessive force on the flap lever. An indication is that you have to slow way down in order to extend full flaps in the landing pattern. The flap lever force may be even higher with full-power prop blast. In a couple of cases, I could not pull the flap lever hard enough to push the button that unlocks the ratchet device—and so could not retract full flaps on go-around.)

Closer to Home

After practicing a few go-arounds from approach speed, try another one from normal touchdown airspeed—about 10 percent above full stall and with the power back to near idle.

No need to raise the nose on this late go-around; just hold that touchdown attitude steady while you pour on the horses. Be ready for lots of right rudder requirement. Don't let the airplane yaw.

One more maneuver to try: recovery and go-around after a bad bounce. Climb a little higher for this one. Really, it's just a full-power recovery from a power-off stall. Fly down that simulated final glide path, simulate a flare and reduce power to idle.

Now, imagine that you really botched the touchdown and bounced five, maybe 10 feet back into the air. Hold the touchdown attitude until you get heavy buffeting or until there's the first hint of sudden pitch-down. Then, apply *full* power. Hold the touchdown attitude. Don't lower the nose (and, for sure, do not raise it, either). Work the rudder to hold the nose straight ahead and don't let it roll. Sure, you may descend back to the simulated runway altitude, but nobody ever mandated that a go-around could never touch the runway.

Be careful with this maneuver. You're recovering from near stall *without* the usual reduction in pitch attitude. If you have lots of horse-power under the cowl, a sudden jam of the throttle will be like a sudden slug of lots of left rudder. And that's a good way to start a spin. So, be a little more gentle with the power application.

Another consideration: You're likely to practice these go-around maneuvers either solo or (preferably) with a CFI aboard. Keep in mind that if Old Bessie is a four- or six-seater, performance won't be as good at max gross weight. It won't be as good, either, on a hot day or at a high-altitude airport. You might want to practice the maneuvers again with manifold pressure set two inches less than maximum or with 100 fewer rpm on a fixed-pitch prop. When the aircraft is heavier and/or has less available power, the allowed pitch attitude will be a little less on go-around.

Keep in mind, too, that if your airplane has a turbocharged engine with a simple turbo controller (such as a fixed waste gate), you cannot simply jam the throttle full forward or you will get a bad overboost. Same for most of the turboprops. Better have a good "feel" for throttle position at max allowed power and maybe a pencil or tape mark on the throttle quadrant. Don't count on that overboost warning light or "pop-off" safety valve. Your hand is on the lever, so *you* control the manifold pressure.

Touch-and-Goes

Let's finish up with a discussion of a somewhat related maneuver: the touch-and-go landing.

Many of the same considerations apply, except that you can take the time to retract the flaps and, maybe, add a turn of trim before applying power. But once you do push the throttle forward, the airplane is usually ready to fly. You have lots of residual airspeed.

The biggest error I see on touch-and-goes is pilots "flying" again before they have full takeoff power applied. *That's dangerous!* It is like a half-power go-around. You aren't going to go up very well, and you may stall trying.

I'm all for touch-and-goes, but only on relatively long runways. On a 3,000-foot strip, it's like starting a normal takeoff from the midfield intersection—*not good*. The accident statistics are pretty dismal for late go-arounds from short runways with trees at the upwind end. A similar poor record can be expected of those who play the touch-and-go game at these airports.

To sum up, if some day you do have to get out of there in a hurry, at the last minute, at Mount Pokey Wilderness Strip, you'll probably make it *if you have practiced*. Better yet in such a situation, *plan* on making your go-around earlier. And know the procedures and pitch attitudes *cold*.

IFR pilots are sometimes called upon to land in crosswinds that would leave their VFR brethren grounded. Again, we've covered this topic in earlier volumes, but we'll touch on it again here.

Bill Kelly now discusses a variety of crosswind techniques, including one that was suggested by a reader...and which he recommends against, at least for landing.

Coping With Crosswinds

We don't need statistics to know that landing and takeoff are the riskiest phases of flight. Maneuvering at slow speeds close to the ground is bound to build up the accident tables. If you look, though, you'll find that those tables account for nearly half of all general aviation accidents. Not all of them involve the classic stall/spin on departure or short final, either. A good proportion—one in ten—happen when pilots lose control of their aircraft while they're on the ground, rolling for takeoff or after landing.

Lots of these accidents result from poor technique, but a goodly portion involve pilots who operate in wind conditions that are beyond the capabilities of their aircraft. Managing the two most critical phases of flight requires knowledge and skill in handling crosswinds, and knowing what to do when the wind is more than a match for the pilot or the airplane.

Off Center

The first task is to figure out what you're up against. The answers come from the "wind components" chart in the airplane manual. Plotting wind velocity against the angle formed between the flight path and the wind direction reveals both crosswind and headwind components.

Obviously, looking up the crosswind component for the aircraft you're flying while you are marching down final is unrealistic. It's best to evaluate crosswind limits before you fly. You have to *know* the crosswind reactions of your plane across a spectrum of angles and wind speeds, and then react to the situation.

As the accompanying figure shows, a 30 knot wind oriented 30 degrees to the runway centerline gives you 15 knots of crosswind and about 26 knots of headwind. Rule of thumb: When the wind is blowing at an angle of 30 degrees to the runway, half of its speed is equal to the crosswind component. At 45 degrees, three-quarters works nicely as a rough estimate. And to be safe, especially when there are strong gusts, you might want to consider anything coming from more than 45 degrees as all crosswind.

What's Required

Figuring your limits is a bit more difficult. A good place to start is to check the airplane manual for a "maximum demonstrated crosswind component," which isn't necessarily a limitation. It might have been the strongest crosswind the manufacturer and the FAA could find during certification.

Some manuals include a "maximum recommended" crosswind component, which could be the most the company test pilot could handle after many hours of practice or the result of a conservative decision by the airplane-builder on what the average customer should attempt.

Other manuals might have words such as: "17 knots was the maximum crosswind component experienced during certification but is not considered a limit." Maybe it's not a limitation, but before you attempt that 17-knot crosswind, you had better really know your airplane.The FAA's certification standards merely require that there be no uncontrollable ground- or water-looping tendencies in 90-degree crosswinds up to a velocity equal to 0.2 times the airplane's stall speed in landing configuration (Vso). If the stall speed is 60 knots, for example, the manufacturer only has to demonstrate a crosswind capability of 12 knots.The regs also state that an airplane "must be satisfactorily controllable, without exceptional piloting skill or alertness, in power off landings at normal landing speed, without using brakes or engine power to maintain a straight path," and that it "must have adequate control during taxiing."

What It Means

What does all of this FAA gobbledygook mean to you, the pilot? It's my opinion that you had better believe the "max crosswind" figure published in the flight manual, especially if it is close to the 0.2-times-Vso number. Maybe that figure represents the worst crosswind the FAA test pilots could find. On the other hand, the company, for liability reasons, might not want to tell you that their people could really handle 25 knots with no problem.

Then again, it might also mean that the test pilots had to use "special techniques" to control a takeoff or landing roll at 0.2 Vso. Like maybe reduced flap settings or a wheel landing in a tail-dragger. Some manuals provide such nebulous information as: "When landing in a strong crosswind, use the minimum flap setting required for field length."

Panic Situation

I learned a good lesson about crosswinds during my CFI check ride. The FAA examiner wanted to see my landing technique on a runway that had a 90-degree crosswind blowing right at the AFM number. The runway also had tall trees close by, on the upwind side. I objected. He insisted.

The result? A panic low-altitude go-around! Horrible turbulence, marginal performance with those big barn-door flaps hanging from our old Skyhawk. Big, uncorrectable drift just above runway level, and almost no climb rate.

I think the man from the FAA also learned a lesson that day. Don't mess with limit crosswinds—especially with flaps hanging way down and obstructions nearby to give turbulence beyond your control capabilities. And don't wait till you're 10 feet above the runway to decide whether or not you can make it. Go around if you need to. Don't let the airplane touch down unless everything is perfect. On takeoff, reduce power and slow down if you are having trouble holding direction, if the airplane is starting to slide sideways or if the plane is starting to lean away from the wind.

Crab vs. Slip

Two techniques are commonly used for crosswind landings, and there's a good deal of argument to be made for either one. To avoid subjecting passengers to unusual attitudes, many pilots favor the crab technique. According to one AFM, you "hold a crab angle into the wind until ready to flare out for the landing...then lower the upwind wing to

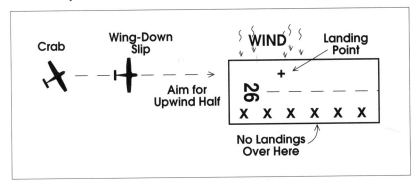

get rid of the crab without drifting...and use the rudder to stay aligned with the runway."

In my book, that's waiting a little too long to determine if you really have enough rudder and aileron control to hold a no-drift/slip-type correction for a crosswind touchdown. If the reported winds or the windsock/tetrahedron show a considerable crosswind, why not transition to the wing-down forward slip way out on final approach? I would prefer to gauge how much slip is needed and the amount of rudder and aileron required to hold the slip while still well above touchdown speed. Sure, the winds will probably slack off a little as you approach touchdown, but the requirement for rudder/aileron control will increase as airspeed is reduced in the landing flare. Check your manual for any cautionary note against prolonged sideslips. In some aircraft, the fuel system can become unported. You might want to set the fuel selector to the high wing in one of these planes even for a short slip. The caveat also can have something to do with loss of elevator authority with full flaps.

Question of Control

If the wind is gusting, figure that you might need at least half of your total aileron control just to counter a sudden sharp-edged gust just before touchdown.

Too many modern airplanes have very poor roll rates at low airspeed in landing configuration. The FARs require a lightplane to be able to roll 60 degrees in 4 seconds in approach configuration. That's only 15 degrees per second with full aileron plus assisting rudder! That's not enough to counter a sudden crosswind increase during landing flare, especially if you are already using half of your aileron travel just to hold a slip. I have probably canceled more flights due to wind than any other weather condition. How many of you always ask for current and forecast surface winds at your destination? It may be CAVU-to-the-moon, but that CAVU stuff often brings the worst winds. We plan alternates for ceilings and visibilities; why not for winds? If all else fails and you don't have the petrol or weather to go elsewhere, it's a good idea to tell ATC you have a problem. Or declare an emergency and do what you have to do—land into the wind on the closed runway, a taxiway or the midfield grass. Don't bust the bird and your passengers by landing in too much crosswind.

Exploring the Arc

In response to an article I wrote about crosswinds, several readers suggested an alternative—a little-known technique called the "downwind arc."

I haven't ground-looped an airplane yet—but I came close to it recently in a rented Cessna 152 while investigating the "arcing" technique at Bartow, Fla. The winds at Bartow Municipal were variable but mostly from 150-180 degrees at 15 knots, gusting to 25. Runway 9L was the only available concrete. The windsock was standing straight out, whipping frequently and swinging through a 60-degree arc. I did not loosen the tie-downs until preflight inspection was complete. I taxied very slowly and made my run-up into the average wind (lots of turnovers occur during downwind/crosswind engine checks). I arced on the takeoff, starting from the downwind side with about a 20-degree cut on the runway centerline—a fairly hard left curve so that I would not depart the right side of the runway and so that centrifugal force to the right would balance out the side force to the left imposed on the airplane by the big crosswind. The wings stayed level, and I wasn't drifting—just following a gentle pilot-induced curve. The "arc" definitely helped control the initial part of the takeoff roll. I straightened out parallel to centerline in the middle of the right (upwind) half of the runway and continued accelerating to liftoff speed. Flaps were fully up to keep the airplane "heavy" on its wheels. It seemed to take forever to accelerate to 10 knots above minimum no-flap liftoff speed; the drag from two-thirds aileron travel probably had a lot to do with the sluggishness. With the extra airspeed, liftoff was "clean"—no skidding tires—and I was rapidly high enough to get rid of the uncoordinated controls.

Beyond Theory

Arcing theory says that I should have continued turning all the way to liftoff. I tried that once and was sorry I did. I approached the left runway

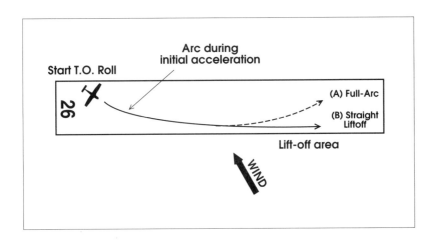

edge far too quickly. My suggestion: "Arc" if you want on takeoff but quit the turning maneuver when you are parallel to the runway and near the upwind edge.

Arcing on landing was not nearly so helpful. In fact, in three tries it always seemed a little on the hairy side. I approached on about a 20-degree angle to centerline but still had to hold considerable right-wing-down slip to fly the path. It was difficult to maintain a no-drift path without the guidance of the centerline and runway edges. Another problem: If I was a little high or a little fast, it was hard to achieve touchdown prior to crossing the centerline. Once on the surface, it was difficult to control a gentle left turn precisely to avoid departing the upwind runway edge or getting too much turn—too much centrifugal force. "Arcing" theory for landing says that you, turn back across the centerline as you slow to taxi speed. That part was scary, and I quit after two tries. It's too easy to get blown off the downwind edge of the pavement. The plane just doesn't want to slow, and it's almost impossible to reverse the turn to get parallel to centerline.

Thumbs Down

With a lot of practice, maybe I could have handled the "arcing" landings better. But even then, when faced with a really bad crosswind, I would do as I've done before—land at an angle to centerline but plan on using only enough turn after touchdown to parallel the centerline before running off the upwind edge.

But the goal of this publication is to improve GA safety, not to recommend procedures that take the average pilot into the realm of test pilot just to extend the crosswind limits of his or her airplane. Therefore, "arc" if you wish on the initial part of a takeoff run, but I heartily recommend that you forget "arcing" for a crosswind landing. It may have worked well a long time ago, when pilots had mile-square grass fields to land on. And though some seaplane pilots, especially those who fly twins, still use the turning technique to compensate for inadequate roll control at low airspeed, it just doesn't appear to be a good idea for landing on relatively short, narrow pavement.

Crosswind Checklist

Here is what I recommend:
• Set up a good traffic pattern. Don't get blown too close or too wide on downwind leg.
• Set up on final approach a good way out. Line up with the upwind edge of the runway and establish an initial crab angle to hold the line-up. Add about half of the gust value to your final approach speed. (If the

reported winds were "20, gusting to 30 knots," for instance, you'd add about five knots.)

• At a quarter to a half mile out on final, transition to a wing-down slip. Get a feel for the amount of bank and control deflection you need to hold a straight path to the upwind edge of the runway. Go around immediately if the corrections are excessive.

• Plan to touch down in the center of the upwind half of the runway. Accept no touchdown that will be downwind of the centerline.

• Don't touch down unless all drift has been compensated for and heading is aligned with the runway.

• Use aileron control to compensate for drift. Use rudder to maintain runway heading.

• Carry enough power to keep the plane flying until you are sure you can maintain complete control through touchdown.

• Plan on making several go-arounds when the winds are really kicking. Repeat: No touchdowns until everything is perfect.

• Keep flying the airplane after touchdown. Ease in the rest of that aileron control and hold a steady heading. Be ready to use brakes for steering.

• For most airplanes, leave the flaps retracted if the winds are near crosswind limits. For sure, use no more than the flap setting recommended for approach or takeoff.

Practice, Practice

If yours is a tail-dragger, good luck. A fly-it-on "wheel" landing will get you down in more crosswind than a three-pointer, but there is still that moment of truth when you run out of speed and have to drop the tail. Better have practiced wheel landings recently. A more realistic personal limit might be the max crosswind you can handle with a three-pointer.

The best bet for any of us—no matter what crosswind technique is preferred—is to get out there and practice. You don't need limit crosswinds. Get good at one-wheel arrivals with the crosswind at only 0.1 Vso. Perfect your technique in the lighter winds and work up slowly into the gusty/limit conditions. Don't wait until you have a load of passengers to practice your technique.

No Excuse

There's no excuse for launching into a gusty crosswind that's more than a match for pilot or plane. If it's hard to hold heading or you have problems keeping the wings level or staying near the centerline while accelerating for takeoff—why not quit?

Don't mess with those big crosswinds. Your airplane is only required to handle 20 percent of its stall speed as a crosswind component. Maybe your airplane has better control than most, and maybe you are a little more proficient than the average pilot; maybe you once made a successful landing with a crosswind of 30 knots, gusting to 45. Please don't try it again. The "averages" are against you.

We'll close the book with a look at the landing, itself, and the rollout. While many pilots of high-performance aircraft tend to land hot, that may not be the best way in all circumstances.

Bill Kelly gives us some pointers on how to avoid driving it on—or dropping it in—too hard.

Avoiding Hard Landings

Flying a lot recently on various airlines, I have become pretty good at anticipating the quality of a landing. Even when seated on the aisle, without an outside view to allow judgment of height above the runway during the landing flare, I can fairly closely estimate just how hard the forthcoming touchdown will be.

I time the interval between power cut and arrival. "One potato, two potato, three potato...." Anything past four potato (i.e., four seconds) is likely to be a "firm" landing.

I'm not knocking the pilots. They have a fairly tough job of it. They're way out ahead of the landing gear, and their eye level is far above the wheels. If the flare is started a little high, the airspeed is a little fast or they're just a tad late in reducing power, that big bird is going to "float" a bit, then descend rapidly.

It's got to be difficult to make a "squeaker." Even if the pilot realizes that he has flared a hair high, he doesn't dare adjust the pitch attitude the way you might in a light airplane in an attempt to readjust the glide path. And the power response from those big turbofans is relatively slow. There's little chance of "saving" a landing by adding power.

Every year or two, I read an account of how an airliner was seriously damaged in a hard landing. But there are on average about a dozen reports of substantial structural damage to general aviation aircraft in hard landings *each and every month.*

That is puzzling, considering that we have a much easier job, in some respects, when it comes to landing a light airplane. We sit right above the main gear and only a few feet above the tires. Our lighter airplanes are a lot more responsive to small elevator control inputs at low airspeed. Our powerplants respond instantly to small throttle increases. Our cockpits provide relatively good visibility, and most allow a good pitch attitude reference over the nose. We usually don't have to "chop" the throttle and use heavy braking and reverse thrust to avoid an over-run.

A good landing depends on a good approach, of course. If you haven't stabilized on the proper airspeed way out on final—and for IFR pilots, that means during the approach—and aren't carrying sufficient power to maintain that airspeed on the desired glide path, you are setting yourself up for a possible poor arrival.

You might flare a little too much, a little too soon, and end up floating five to ten feet above the runway. It's difficult to touch down gracefully from such a position.

If you drop the nose, you might arrive sooner than you expected and land hard in a three-point or nose-wheel-first attitude. If you add just the right amount of power and hold the proper pitch attitude, you just might make a decent landing out of it. But, add too much power and you may float too far down the runway or "balloon" even higher.

It bears repeating that a decelerating final puts you at risk of running out of airspeed during the flare and touching down hard on the concrete or the terrain short of the runway.

Most, but not all, general aviation airplanes have enough excess energy at 1.3 Vso (airspeed 30 percent above landing configuration stall speed) to flare from a steep idle-power glide.

At the same airspeed but in a shallower (say, three-degree) power-on descent, the airplane will tend to exhibit a little more float even with power reduced to idle during the flare. But if you coordinate the flare with gentle throttle reduction, that little bit of excess air time will allow setting the proper touchdown attitude while descending gently onto the concrete.

I constantly remind students that there are *four* flight controls: elevators, ailerons, rudder and throttle. All pilots tend to be lazy when it comes to using the throttle properly. For takeoff, set and hold full power. For cruise, set cruise power. But on final approach, that throttle hand had better be ready to fly, just like the other hand on the wheel or stick.

And during that short period when the airplane is held off the runway just before touchdown, that throttle hand had better be ready to add some power *before* the bottom drops out, in case the airplane was flared too high.

Behind the Power Curve

Induced drag increases substantially during the landing flare, especially if you are shooting for a touchdown with the proper attitude and low airspeed.

Your airplane is getting onto the backside of the power curve. That's fine if the wheels are only a foot or two from the pavement. But if you are still five or ten feet high, the deficiency in thrust is going to cause a very high rate of descent before the wheels finally touch. The only remedy in this case is *immediate* and *sufficient* power application.

In fact, if you have any doubt about your height above the runway, apply *full* power and go around.

Unfortunately, we all have an instinctive reaction to the seat-of-the-pants sensation that the airplane is starting to fall: We raise the nose in an attempt to arrest the increased descent rate. Meanwhile, though, the throttle hand remains inactive. The result is a further increase in induced drag and descent rate. The airplane bangs onto the runway in an excessive nose-high pitch attitude and very close to stalling. Another hard landing goes into the files.

What you might want to tell yourself, then, while you're still way out there on final approach is: "I intend to flare carefully and slowly *only* to the proper pitch attitude for touchdown. Then, if I have not already touched down, I will add power."

That's right. Plan to cushion every touchdown with a little extra power once you have achieved the proper attitude. Nine times out of ten, you will touch down before adding that tad of power. But that tenth one might register a seven on the Richter scale if you don't add power in time.

And, very important, once you have added power to cushion a high flare, don't reduce it again until you have touched down. By all means, don't chop the throttle back to idle.

Flare Management

Keep in mind that a good landing is not always a squeaker. There should be just a bit of "firmness" to your arrival.

Done properly, your descent rate on final approach (say, 400 to 800 fpm) should be reduced slowly during the flare to almost, but not quite, zero. That's right, do *not* try to flare to zero descent rate. That only leads to a hold-off and a hard touchdown if you are too high and don't apply power.

It's better to let the airplane land while in a *controlled* but very shallow descent. That's much better than flaring to zero descent rate, then dropping to the concrete.

Seaplane pilots learn to land on "glassy" water, where the surface is hard to discern from the air. The airplane is flared rapidly to touchdown attitude. Then enough power is added to enable a 100- to 150-fpm descent while holding the proper attitude and low airspeed. This technique is useful for making a relatively soft touchdown on a wide runway after losing your landing light on a dark night.

Your landing gear has oleos, spring-metal struts or rubber bungees for shock absorption. The gear can accommodate a minimal descent rate on every touchdown. Navy carrier planes are designed to land without flaring from a rather steep descent (nominally, about 720 fpm). We certainly don't want to land our general aviation airplanes unflared. But we don't have to flare to a zero descent rate before rolling the tires, either.

If you just have to impress your passengers with squeakers, you really should land on relatively long runways and always with a little power all the way to touchdown. Better yet, brief your fellow fliers to expect a little thump on landing. Tell them that's the right way to do it, that it's the way airline pilots do it.

Indeed, airline pilots do not try to land from a zero descent rate. They shoot for a continuous slight descent rate all the way to touchdown. Those big *kerwhumps* come only when they inadvertently get descent rate to zero while still far above the tarmac.

Full-Stall Fallacy

You really do *not* want to make a "full-stall" landing. In fact, quite a few airplanes will not stall fully when close to the surface. Ground effect, which sometimes seems to cushion your landing or prolong your float due to drag reduction, also makes your up-elevator control less effective due to the reduction in down wash angle.

Without that downward flow onto the top of the horizontal stabilizer surface, you may not have enough elevator to achieve stall angle of attack. Worse yet, if the airplane is nose-heavy and at idle power, you might have trouble reaching a safe nose-up landing attitude.

A full-stall landing, if achieved more than just a few inches above the runway, is sure to result in a hard landing in a funny attitude. Recall what happens when you perform a power-idle stall at altitude. When the wing stalls, the nose drops.

When you are landing, you sure don't want the nose to drop while you are holding lots of back wheel and feeling for the runway. The nose wheel probably would hit the runway first—and hard. In a taildragger, the mains would hit hard, causing a nose-high ricochet. The airplane would then be several feet off the runway with no lift remaining and little, if any, aileron or elevator control.

Even in its three-point attitude, a taildragger is designed to be at slightly less than the wing's stall angle of attack. The only way you could land it full-stall would be tail-wheel-first, with the mains still above the concrete.

Remember, a stalled airplane is partially out of control. That's no way to be landing. Land slow? By all means. Close to stall? Sure, if you have it under control. A typical touchdown speed is about ten percent above stall speed. Don't try to get any slower than that. You may bend the bird if it stalls while still up in the air.

Don't Push It

A lot of accidents happen when airplanes cross the numbers with too much airspeed and pilots try to push them onto the runway. Usually, the nose wheel hits first.

But that nose strut was designed to keep the propeller clear of the ground while taxiing and, in most cases, to provide steering capability. It was not designed to absorb much landing shock.

Don't ever land until you have the proper touchdown attitude. Set that attitude during the latter part of your landing flare and hold it steady. Don't let the nose drop, and don't raise it any higher than the proper attitude.

What is the "proper" touchdown attitude? In a taildragger, it most likely is just a little more nose-up than what you see while taxiing. This doesn't hold for a trike, though. A good approximation is where the trike's nose (the cowling) just barely touches the horizon at the far end of the airport—where the ground meets the sky (assuming level, unobstructed terrain) or where the far end of the runway is just barely visible over the nose.

Some airplanes, such as short-nose twins, require use of the top of the glareshield or the third rivet from the bottom on the windshield post for pitch attitude reference.

Of course, seating position is important. If you sit too low, you won't be able to see over the nose when the proper pitch attitude is established. You will have a tendency to take off and land in a flat attitude. If there's not enough seat adjustment to compensate, then sit on a cushion.

In most light planes, you don't want much more than about one fist (about four inches) of clearance between your head and the cabin ceiling.

Design Traps

There are a few airplanes that were not designed to allow you a view ahead in touchdown attitude, no matter how many cushions you sit on. They are accident statistics waiting to be tallied. The pilot of one of these big nose jobs has to be especially careful that he gets close enough to the runway before setting touchdown attitude.

Another airplane characteristic that can mean trouble on landing is excessive *longitudinal static stability*. This can require a heavy pull on the control wheel and lots of retrimming to slow from final approach speed in the flare and hold the touchdown attitude. Sometimes two hands are required on the wheel for touchdown. (The Cessna 182 and 210, and the Piper Seneca are among the airplanes I've found to be "heavy-handed.")

Some airplanes have very strong *power stability*. This is evident when you add a little power on final to correct your flight path and the nose pitches up strongly enough that you have to retrim. It also shows when you reduce power in the landing flare and wheel pull force increases enough that you have to retrim.

Neither of these characteristics is good. Ideally, you should be able to put down the last "notch" of flaps way out on final, set your approach speed and power, and make one final elevator trim adjustment. From there to touchdown, the throttle hand should stay on the throttle.

But if the airplane you fly exhibits the characteristics of excessive longitudinal static stability or power stability on landing, a stabilized final approach is critical. Get the airspeed established early—with the final flap setting. Get the power adjusted early to hold this speed. That way, you will have to make a minimum of trim and power changes as you approach the runway and start the flare.

One technique I've found to make landings a little more pleasant in heavy-handed airplanes is to use less than full flaps. Wheel force is lower as speed diminishes during the flare, and it's easier to hold the nose up in the touchdown attitude.

Crosswinds and Ice

A leading contender for a record in causing damage on touchdown is the botched crosswind landing.

Most pilots carry a little extra airspeed on final. The old rule of thumb about using normal approach speed plus half of the wind gust value is still viable. But, remember, that extra airspeed is going to mean a little more float if you are sloppy in the flare. And during the flare you are going to be searching for the right amount of aileron control to counter drift. It is easy to get hung up five feet in the air, floating and decelerating rapidly. As airspeed decreases, the required amount of aileron and rudder deflection *increases*.

If crosswind correction isn't perfect and the airplane is allowed to drop in, the landing gear suffer horrible vertical and side loads. Best to have added a little power during the flare—enough to keep the airplane flying at a safe speed. Also, keep the nose just a hair *lower* than the usual touchdown attitude while you seek perfection in your crosswind correction.

Be very careful if there's even a trace of ice on the leading edge of the wing. Carry some power and a little extra speed on final, keep the glide path steeper and higher than usual, and try not to use any flaps.

Carry the power clear to touchdown. Ice adds a lot of drag. If you chop the power, that extra drag is going to bring you down in a hurry. The ice may play heck with stall speeds and characteristics. Stall may come at a much lower angle of attack, and extending flaps may aggravate the problem.

Nailing the Airspeed

Using the right speed on final approach is a key to a good landing.

If your airplane tends to float for quite a few seconds prior to touchdown, you may be flying too fast on final. Many airplane manuals and handbooks quote a final-approach airspeed in the "Normal Procedures" section that's based on gross weight. But in the "Performance" section, you may find *lower* airspeeds recommended for lighter weights.

If not, go up to altitude and perform several power-off stalls in landing configuration. Note the speed at which the nose drops uncontrollably (probably with full-back control wheel at light/forward c.g. loading). Let's say the indicated speed at which the airplane stalls is 50 mph. Multiplying 50 by 1.3 gives us 65 mph. Next, try a few approaches with final approach airspeed stabilized at 65 mph and see if that works better than what you'd been using.

Mind Those Struts

Our final consideration is those oleo struts. Lots of damage is done when airplanes are landed or even taxied on improperly serviced oleo struts.

A strut has air or nitrogen and hydraulic fluid inside. The gas serves as the spring, the fluid as the shock absorber. Too many times, when a pilot complains about a "low" oleo, the solution is to wheel out the high pressure oxygen or nitrogen cart and "blow" the strut back up.

It may look good after that, but what if the strut was low because some of the hydraulic fluid leaked out past worn seals? All that added gas simply replaced missing liquid, and it can't do any shock-absorbing.

Proper strut servicing includes checking the liquid level as well as adding the proper amount of gas. Lack of shock-absorbing capability can easily turn what would have been only a "thumper" landing into one that goes "crunch" as the strut bottoms and excessive forces are transmitted to the gear attach area, wings and fuselage.

The factory-built, certificated airplane that you fly underwent some rather vigorous landing gear drop tests during its development. But there was probably no "fatigue" testing for the possible effects of years of both good and bad landings. Even though the design passed its drop tests and engineering analysis with flying colors, the main gear may still fail some day with a landing load below the ultimate.

I believe very few cases in which airplanes are substantially damaged in hard landings are reported to the National Transportation Safety Board. Too often, even if the airplane can't be taxied back to the ramp after a bad landing, it is "dollied" to the repair shop with nary a word to anyone, except the insurance carriers.

Almost nobody does a post-flight inspection anymore, even after a landing that goes *kerwham!* The trouble is that, many flights later, an unsuspecting pilot may have a gear fold during what he considered only a slightly rough touchdown.

Therefore, why not treat every landing as though that landing gear has *already been damaged* and needs to be treated gently? You don't have to have a squeaker each time, but you should shoot for a gentle "thump" from a continuous shallow descent.

The last article is of particular interest to instrument pilots since, unlike VFR pilots, we routinely land on runway surfaces that are slippery. This is a tough nut to crack, since most AFMs are silent on the subject of braking performance when the runway is slippery.

That makes sense, simply because there's no telling how slippery a runway can be, and it can vary from end-to-end. The tower's call of "Good," "Fair," "Poor," or "Nil" isn't much help, either: the categories are too broad.

Bill Kelly puts on his test pilot hat again for this article.

Getting on the Binders

Most of us have never had to use absolute maximum braking for an emergency stop on the runway. On those occasions when one of us does try to get maximum brake performance, it's not uncommon that one or both main wheels lock up, causing the tire(s) to skid and the airplane to depart the runway, particularly when the weather is lousy and the runway surface offers little friction.

When such mishaps result in bent metal and/or injury, the official determination usually is that the pilot-in-command "failed to maintain directional control." Even when hard braking lasts for only a split second, it's not all that unusual for a post-flight inspection to reveal a "bald spot" where the wheel stopped rotating and the tire lost a lot of rubber from one place on the tread. It was close to a blown tire, but not quite.

There's a lot of technique involved in obtaining maximum braking without locking up a wheel. Those landing distance and accelerate/stop distance charts and graphs in your aircraft flight manual (AFM) were derived using special braking techniques employed by test pilots.

It's not unusual for an aircraft manufacturer's test pilot to go through several sets of tires and, maybe, a change of brakes just practicing to achieve the shortest possible stopping distance for the certification data.

But, can you achieve the same results? There's no way. In fact, you'd be much better off to add 50 percent to whatever landing roll or accelerate/stop distances your AFM shows.

And, that's only for the "paved, level, dry runway" usually specified by the fine print on your AFM charts or graphs. The landing distance chart in the Cessna 182R "information manual," for example, has a note saying, "For operation on a dry, grass runway, increase distances by 40 percent of the 'ground-roll' figure."

That's fine, but how about long grass? Wet grass? Dirt or gravel?

Unfortunately, a lot of the available short strips aren't the good brush-finished concrete or macadam which give the maximum "coefficient of friction" for braking.

And, in most cases, how much distance you will need to land on a grass or dirt strip is strictly a guess.

That said, let's begin our exploration of braking "theory" by taking a look at Figure 1, a graph of braking coefficient of friction for several different concrete runway surface conditions versus percent of tire slippage.

(Tire slippage is zero if the tire is rolling with no wheel braking. If the airplane is moving at 60 mph on the runway but the rim of the tire is only turning at a rim speed of 55 mph under braking, then you have about 10 percent tire slippage. Slippage reaches 100 percent when the wheel is fully locked and the tire is skidding.)

The graph curves in Figure 1 look a little familiar, don't they? Like a graph of coefficient of lift versus angle of attack, maybe, where the "peak" means wing stall?

Let's look at those braking curves more closely: Note that the friction coefficients rise rapidly on the far left sides of the graph curves and, then, peak prior to 10 percent slip.

Avoiding Slippage

That peak in friction coefficient is where you have to apply just the right amount of brake pedal pressure to achieve maximum braking.

Too little pedal pressure, and your braking friction coefficient is less than the maximum; however, it's still on the front side of the graph—to the far left and short of 10 percent slip, even on dry concrete.

But, that's where all of your normal stops should be. Let's talk about "normal" stops before we get further into max braking.

With only a low amount (percent) of tire slippage, there will be little tire wear and, since you get stopped fairly quickly, relatively little heating of the brakes, wheels and tires. Also, there's less chance that you will lock up one wheel, then have directional control and/or blown tire problems.

So, for normal landings on a decent length of runway, take it easy on the brakes. And, if you don't intend to use hard braking, do not retract the flaps in an attempt to get more weight on the wheels to assist braking. The aerodynamic drag from extended flaps will give a lot of initial deceleration from touchdown speed and, thus, save on need for

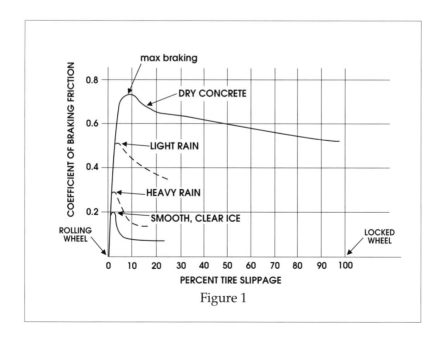

Figure 1

wheel braking.

The effect is almost the same as from the big speed brakes or spoilers that extend right after touchdown on many airline and corporate jets, or the drag chute that pops out right after touchdown from some of the jet fighters and the space shuttle.

Let's go back to Figure 1 again, specifically to the top curve (for "dry concrete"), and talk about maximum braking. This graph is from H.H. Hurt's Aerodynamics for Naval Aviators and applies to a particular airplane, a particular runway surface, a specific tire rubber composition and tire tread pattern—all factors that affect the braking coefficient of friction.

From this graph curve, we can see that max braking friction coefficient is approximately 0.7 at a tire slip of about 8 percent. Anything less than 8 percent slip, and you don't have max braking.

Edge of Disaster

But, suppose that you overdo the pressure on the brake pedals and slow the wheels to where you have 50 percent tire slippage on the runway surface.

In this case, you still have a pretty good braking friction coefficient (0.6); so, still lots of stopping power.

The trouble with over-braking is that you are right on the edge of disaster. The wheels are still rotating, but with a tire rim speed that's only half of your ground speed on the runway. There's lots of black streak being left on the runway and, thus, extreme tire wear.

But, that's not your most serious problem. The biggest problem is that you are into an "unstable" region of brake pedal manipulation. It's sort of like trying to fly at a slightly higher angle of attack than wing stall angle. Sure, you can barely hang on to some airplanes with the control wheel full back, as the airplane rapidly falls with ailerons and rudder just about run out of effectiveness. Add just a little too much rudder and/or aileron, or delay just a little in reducing a control input, and you get (you guessed it) a spin.

Loss of control is what you're close to when you overdo the pressure on brake pedals and get onto the back side of the braking friction coefficient curve. You are very close to locking a wheel, losing braking friction coefficient and skidding—and, maybe, blowing a tire.

If you ever have to use hard braking and begin to encounter a directional control problem, get off of the brake pedals. Then, start again—a little more gently.

If you ever feel an initial good deceleration from hard braking, then suddenly sense a decrease in deceleration, get off of the brakes. What you are feeling is one or both tires at, or approaching, a locked-wheel condition (100 percent tire slippage).

Once you get on the back side of the braking friction coefficient curve, you have to relax brake pressure, or the tire rpm will probably continue to decrease more rapidly than your airplane's speed on the runway; the percentage of tire slippage will continue to increase—right to a locked wheel.

Professor Hurt also points out that in this "incipient skid" condition, with a high percentage of tire slippage (even before full skid), the tires aren't capable of providing any significant side force. Thus, the airplane may not want to keep going where the tires are pointing; you may drift sideways, as though you were driving a car on glare ice.

Slippery Situations

Back to Figure 1 again—this time, to look at the graph curves for light rain, heavy rain and smooth, clear ice on that concrete runway.

Note that even a slightly wet runway can reduce your braking friction coefficient by approximately 30 percent. The curve for heavy rain shows about a 60 percent reduction in braking—and this is even before we get into hydroplaning, a situation in which the tire can't even penetrate the water film to touch the concrete.

If your tires ever should begin to hydroplane, your braking coefficient of friction is likely to be even less than shown by the curve for smooth, clear ice in Figure 1. There won't be any braking until the airplane has slowed and the tires finally touch the concrete.

Hydroplaning has a lot to do with the total bottom tire surface area trying to make contact with the runway. Big, fat tires and/or low tire pressure make you more susceptible to hydroplaning. (It's sort of like water skiing, except that you don't have the tow rope to keep you going straight.)

Should you worry about the possibility of hydroplaning? Probably not, if you don't insist on landing in the midst of a heavy rain shower.

Just like highways, the runways at major airports are built with a slight "crown" (i.e., the center of the runway is slightly higher than the edges) to allow water to run off. Some of them are grooved to allow even better run-off.

But, if you try to land while it's still raining heavily and the water is forming a film above the runway surface, yes, you could have a problem with hydroplaning.

In that case, don't count on any braking until the airplane has slowed greatly. And, figure that you might be blown off the side of the runway if there's any crosswind. Directional control is apt to be nil—no control from the wheel brakes and, maybe, no nose wheel steering control if the front tire is also "skiing" on a thick film of water.

A more likely problem is that short, narrow strip at Dogpatch Regional—that old dirt strip the county road department paved with leftover macadam after refinishing Route 34.

It may have no crown and, thus, poor water run-off. It may even have reverse-crown areas where water puddles, even after the rain has stopped falling.

Running through even a shallow puddle while still at high speed and with heavy braking applied is likely to put you into instantaneous wheel lock-up. And then, maybe, sudden blown tires when you exit the puddle onto dry hardtop. Best bet: Get off the brakes before you go through a puddle.

We wouldn't have to be all that concerned about braking if all of our airplanes were equipped with anti-skid brake systems. An anti-skid system automatically senses wheel speed and modulates brake pressure to prevent wheel lock-up, while still providing maximum braking friction coefficient.

All the modern airliners and most of our corporate jets have such systems. Anti-skid systems also are available in many new automobiles. But, for most GA airplanes? Not yet.

Since most of us don't have anti-skid systems to help out, let's consider how we can get maximum braking without leaving rubber on the runway or leaving the runway entirely:

Having done a number of aircraft certification tests for landing-distance and accelerate/stop performance, I have had a lot of practice in maximum braking. And, I've blown a few tires. But, I have learned a lot about modulating ankle-effort on the brake pedals and "sensing" airplane deceleration.

Also, I've learned that each airplane is different. Each brake type is different. There are differences even with a change in brake pad material or runway surface condition and temperature.

Installation of big "tundra" tires can greatly reduce the effectiveness of your wheel brakes. And, I wonder whether some of those after-market stainless and chromed brake disks are really as good as what was originally certified.

Emergency Stops

Let's imagine that you are "committed": Either you are going to land at Dogpatch, regardless of its short runway, or you have decided to abort the takeoff out of Dogpatch because the engine coughed.

Either way, you need maximum braking. Here are some pointers:

1. If it's a landing, land on-speed—as slow as possible. If it's a bad final approach—high and/or fast—go around and try again.

2. Get maximum weight on the main wheels. On some airplanes, this will mean retracting the flaps (this, after all, is not a normal landing); follow your AFM recommendations. Let the nose wheel go down onto the runway, to reduce angle of attack and wing lift.

3. Come on slowly with brake pedal pressure. Keep increasing pedal pressure until you can sense a good deceleration. You're shooting for no more than the maximum braking friction coefficient from Figure 1 for the surface condition; but, settle for only 75 percent of that, because you haven't practiced and probably won't be able to get the maximum without overshooting to the back side of the braking friction coefficient curve.

4. As you increase braking, come in with full-back control wheel or stick. This will transfer more of the airplane weight to the main gear of a tricycle-gear airplane and, thus, give you more braking friction coefficient for stopping. If it's a taildragger, the up-elevator will help hold the tail end down. However, remember that as your taildragger gets slower, the elevators will lose effectiveness but the brakes won't; so, you may have to ease off on the pedal pressure to prevent a nose-over.

5. If you have stayed on the front side of the curve, you'll be able to sense changes in deceleration and modulate brake pedal pressure accordingly. If you're halfway to a stop and deceleration decreases, increase pedal pressure slightly. Very important: If deceleration increases, decrease the pedal pressure just a bit, before you go past the peak braking friction coefficient and onto the back side of the curve.

6. If you ever sense a sudden yaw or a sudden loss of all deceleration, let go of the brake pedals. Then, start again gently.

7. Don't intentionally apply brake pressure intermittently. The short intervals between applications won't allow any useful brake cooling (the brakes were certified for max continuous braking, anyway). Also, each initial application of pedal pressure is just another chance to overdo the braking and get into an incipient skid. You can feel deceleration better with steady braking. It's this "feel" that the test pilot used to get the manufacturer's wonderful AFM stopping data.

8. If there's any doubt about getting stopped, kill the engine. Your propeller is probably providing zero or slightly negative thrust when at idle at touchdown speed, but it's giving considerable forward thrust as you slow to taxi speeds.

9. Be careful while taxiing back to the parking area. There is such a thing as "brake fade" with red-hot brake disks, especially with some of

the older pad materials. Go slowly, at minimum power and without using brakes. Give the brakes a chance to cool a bit before you get to the tie-down. Then, do not set the parking brake, because there's a good chance you will warp the hot brake disks or, maybe, weld some components together.

10. Don't crawl under the wing right after shut-down to inspect the brakes and tires. If you really made a maximum-effort stop from high speed, the brakes will be hot. And, they will be transferring their heat to the wheels and tires. An explosive blowout is possible; and, the higher the tire pressure, the more dangerous it will be. Stay away until the wheels and tires have cooled.

Perils of Practice

That has been a lot of words about how to use your brakes for a hard stop. Now that we've absorbed some of the "theory" behind maximum braking, let's consider whether we should actually go out and practice in "Old Bessie."

Well, I'm not sure. It's like the argument concerning spin training: Will there be more accidents during the training than "saves" from inadvertent spins, thanks to the training?

For the record, I'm in favor of spin training. In the case of maximum-effort braking, I would favor some training or individual practice, but not from high-speed conditions. Even in "Old Bessie" or "Belchfire," just one max accelerate/slow-down from 20 knots slower than touch-

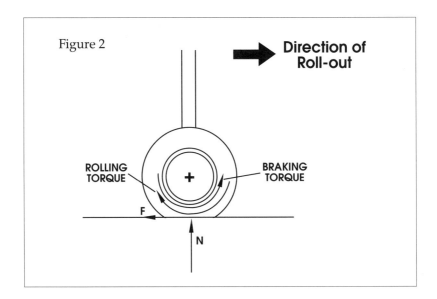

Figure 2

Direction of Roll-out

ROLLING TORQUE

BRAKING TORQUE

+

F

N

down speed to taxi speed might teach a lot about brake pedal application.

Don't worry about ruining your brakes. If you're flying one of the newer models, you won't be able to even measure any wear, and you might even break in your pads to where they are more capable.

Next time you get new brake pads installed, check the installation instructions; you might even find that such heavy initial brake application is desired to "condition" the pads.

Before we conclude our exploration of braking, here's just a little more on "theory." Look at Figure 3, an illustration of a main wheel rolling to the right.

"N" represents normal force—airplane weight minus any aerodynamic lift, plus any weight shift to the main gear from holding up-elevator. "F" is the friction retarding force you can develop when you start braking.

F divided by N is our braking friction coefficient from Figure 1. The tire friction force (F) develops a "rolling torque" in the wheel and tire which we are opposing with a "braking torque" from brake pedal application.

So long as we apply brake pedal pressure to keep braking torque equal to or less than maximum available rolling torque, braking will be satisfactory. But, let braking torque exceed the max available rolling torque, and the wheel will slow down until it's stationary ("locked wheel").

Let's conclude with a few general considerations about brakes and braking:

First, remember that the brakes are part of the landing gear. Those of you who fly retractable-gear airplanes always check "gear down" before landing, don't you? But, do you also check the brake pedals for equal pressure on both sides? And, do you check that the parking brake is off?

Same goes for you "fixed-gear" fliers: There should be a "U" even in your GUMPF check or AFM checklist. Check the pedals and parking brake knob/lever, even though you don't have to extend the gear.

Several years ago, an FAA test pilot had an embarrassing experience (almost a nose-over) during certification tests of a high-power taildragger. It seems that the parking brake had been partially applied for the engine run-up but not released thereafter. With all its power, the airplane made the takeoff OK with the parking brake knob still out and the brakes still partly on. But, at the end of the landing roll, that light brake application was enough to lift the tailwheel until the prop ticked the runway.

So, why not add "brakes" to your takeoff and landing checklists?

One final thought: If you depart from a wet or slushy runway, don't be in a hurry to retract the wheels; give that 100-knot wind stream a chance to dry your brakes before you tuck the wheels into their wells.

Index

S

T

U